STUDY GUIDE

to accompany

Susan A. Nolan • Thomas E. Heinzen
Essentials of Statistics for the Behavioral Sciences

Jennifer Coleman
Western New Mexico University

Robert Weathersby
Eastern University

Robin Freyberg
Stern College for Women
Yeshiva University

WORTH PUBLISHERS

Study Guide
by Jennifer Coleman, Robert Weathersby, and Robin Freyberg
to accompany
Susan A. Nolan and Thomas E. Heinzen: *Essentials of Statistics for the Behavioral Sciences*

ISBN-10: 1-4292-2831-8
ISBN-13: 978-1-4292-2831-2

Printed in the United States of America

Second Printing 2010

Worth Publishers
41 Madison Avenue
New York, NY 10010
www.worthpublishers.com

CONTENTS

PREFACE

This **_Study Guide_** is designed for use with _Essentials of Statistics for the Behavioral Sciences_ by Susan A. Nolan and Thomas E. Heinzen. It is intended to help you learn the material in the textbook, evaluate your understanding of that material, and to review any problem areas you may have. Each chapter contains an outline, learning objectives, a chapter review (organized by major textbook section), and study questions accompanied by correct answers and text page references, all designed to help you master introductory statistics.

If you read the textbook and this study guide actively, working through the exercises in each chapter, you should find that the material covered is accessible to you. We encourage you to revisit the material from time to time, as you might learn something new with each review. Statistics is a subject that can be intimidating to students, but you are taking this class because it is relevant to you and to the work you want to do. You already know a great deal about statistics, as you are exposed to them in your classes, on the Internet, and on television every day. You might even be surprised to know that you report statistical claims when you discuss sports or trends in the workplace and in relationships. The textbook and the study guide will help you understand those statistics better and put the language of statistics to work for you.

Acknowledgments

We would like to thank the Worth Publishers team, including Christine Burak, Jenny Chiu, and Stacey Alexander for their dedication in coordinating various aspects of the editorial and production processes.

Jennifer Coleman
Robert Weathersby
Robin Freyberg

CHAPTER 1

An Introduction to Statistics and Research Design

CHAPTER OUTLINE

The Two Branches of Statistics
- Descriptive Statistics
- Inferential Statistics
- Distinguishing Between a Sample and a Population

How to Transform Observations into Variables
- Discrete Observations
- Continuous Observations

Three Types of Variables
- Independent, Dependent, and Confounding Variables
- Reliability and Validity

Introduction to Hypothesis Testing
- Conducting Experiments to Control for Confounding Variables
- Between-Groups Design versus Within-Groups Design
- Correlational Research

LEARNING OBJECTIVES

After studying this chapter, you should be able to:

1. Define each of the following terms and provide examples that are not in the text: *variable*; *discrete observations* and *continuous observations*; *nominal*, *ordinal*, *interval* and *ratio variable*; *scale variable*; *levels*; *independent*, *dependent*, and *confounding*; *reliability* and *validity*; *hypothesis testing*, *operational definition*, *experiment*, *random assignment*; *correlation and correlational studies*; and *between-* and *within-groups research design*.

2. Distinguish between descriptive and inferential statistics, as well as between samples and populations by defining and providing examples of each.

3. Describe the process of *hypothesis testing* in terms of its purpose, underlying logic, and methodology. Your description should display an

1

understanding of the basic vocabulary of research design, including the manipulation or observation of *independent variables* and the measurement of *dependent variables*—including an assessment of their *reliability* and *validity*—in the context of a research design in which *confounding variables* are controlled or at least accounted for.

4. Explain the essential (defining) differences between *experiments* and *correlational studies*, and describe the general circumstances under which researchers might employ each one in the practice of *hypothesis testing*.

5. Compare and contrast *between-* and *within-groups research designs*.

CHAPTER REVIEW

> The Two Branches of Statistics

The text that this study guide accompanies is about the ways in which behavioral and social scientists use statistics in the service of asking and answering questions about individuals, groups, and the social environment. It is about the application of statistics to solve research problems in the social and behavioral sciences. There are two major branches, or divisions, of statistics: **descriptive statistics** and **inferential statistics**. The purpose of descriptive statistics is to organize, summarize, and communicate detailed information about a collection of numbers called data. Note that a descriptive statistical analysis can include the calculation of statistics, such as an average, as a way of summarizing data.

The goal of most research in the social and behavioral sciences is to use the information in a sample of data to form a conclusion—that is, make an *inference*—about an entire population. This process of using the information in a sample to make an inference about a population defines the task of inferential statistics. A **sample** is a set of data that a researcher has collected from a much larger set of data called a **population**. Ideally, the sample should be representative of the population.

> How to Transform Observations into Variables

The term *data* was described briefly above as a collection of numbers. These numbers are obtained by observing, or measuring, the variable. A **variable**, in turn, is any characteristic of the unit of study (typically a person) that varies. Researchers use the terms *data*, *measures*, and *observations* somewhat interchangeably, but in each instance they are referring to the values of a variable.

Variables may be categorized as either **discrete** or **continuous**, depending upon limits imposed by the scale of measurement. The values of discrete variables are always integers and usually whole numbers, whereas continuous variables have values that are, at least conceptually, unlimited. Variables measured on a nominal or ordinal scale are always discrete[1], whereas interval and ratio variables may be either discrete or continuous. The rule of thumb is this: Continuous variables may have fractional values but discrete variables may not.

Variables are most basically classified according to one of the four scales applied to measure them: **nominal, ordinal, interval**, and **ratio**. The scale names are listed according to the level of quantitative precision they represent. Thus a nominal scale represents the lowest level of quantitative precision (none at all), whereas the ratio scale represents the highest level. (The French word "noir" is a useful mnemonic to help you remember this order.) Identifying a variable's scale of measurement determines the statistical test used for data analysis.

The values of **nominal variables** are names or labels. For example, the values "female" and "male" represent different categories of the nominal variable gender. The only property of the real number system used in a nominal scale of measurement is the property of *difference*. Coded values (e.g., "1" = "female" and "2" = "male") have the appearance of quantity but reflect only qualitative difference.

The values of **ordinal variables** are usually ranks (e.g., class rank or order of finish). The values of ordinal variables may also be codes (e.g., 0 = *never*, 1 = *weekly*, and 2 = *daily*) representing differences in responses to a question about the frequency of some behavior such as: "How often do you read the newspaper?" The ordinal scale includes the properties of difference ($1 \neq 2$) and magnitude ($1 < 2$).

Most variables studied by psychologists are regarded as **interval variables**. The interval scale includes the number system properties of *difference* ($1 \neq 2$), *magnitude* ($1 < 2$), and *equal intervals* ($2 - 1 = 3 - 2$).

The most sophisticated scale of measurement is used to measure **ratio variables**. Examples of ratio variables include any variable whose values are counts, such as number of siblings and number of times engaging in a particular behavior. Physical measurements such as height, weight, time (age, reaction time, number of hours worked per week) are also ratio variables. The ratio scale of measurement includes the number system properties of *difference* ($1 \neq 2$), *magnitude* ($1 < 2$), *equal intervals* ($2 - 1 = 3 - 2$), and an absolute zero scale value that permits ratio comparisons ($8 / 4 = 4 / 2$). The distinction between these scales is not important for most statistical analyses. For example, SPSS[2] refers to ratio and interval variables as **scale** variables, because the same statistical procedures are used to analyze the values of either type of variable. Similarities and distinctions among the four scales of measurement are summarized in Table 1.

---

[1] An exception to this general rule is the use of fractional ranks to resolve ties. For example, two individuals who "tie" for second place might each be assigned the rank of 2.5: $(2 + 3) / 2 = 2.5$.
[2] According to the company's Web site, SPSS was an acronym for "Statistical Package for the Social Sciences" when the company was founded in 1968. The computer program is now known simply as "SPSS" and the company is "SPSS, Inc." Familiarity, if not facility, with this software is expected by most graduate programs in the social and behavioral sciences.

Table 1 *Differences between the four types of variables in terms of the scales used to measure them*

Scale	Scale Properties	Example of Scale Properties	Example of Variable Illustrating Scale Properties
Nominal	Difference	1 = "fiction" 2 = "nonfiction" $1 \neq 2$	A person who reads fiction is expressing a preference that *differs* from that of a person who reads nonfiction.
Ordinal	Difference Magnitude	1 = "1 or 2 books a year" 2 = "at least 1 book each week" $1 < 2, 2 > 1$	A person who reads "at least 1 book each week" reads a *greater* number of books than a person who reads "1 or 2 books a year."
Interval	Difference Magnitude Equal Intervals	$2 - 1 = 3 - 2$	The difference between reading 2 books a week and 1 book a week is the same as the difference between reading 3 books a week and 2 books a week.
Ratio	Difference Magnitude Equal Intervals Absolute Zero (enables ratio comparisons)	$4 / 2 = 2 / 1$	A person who reads 4 books a week reads twice as many books as a person who reads 2 books a week, etc.

> Three Types of Variables

When describing variables, we often discuss **levels**, which are values or conditions that the variable can take on.

Variables are also categorized according to their functional role in research designs. An **independent variable** is conceptualized as the "cause" whereas a **dependent variable** is measured as the "effect" of that cause. A third category of variables, called **confounding variables**, produce effects that may be mixed up, or *confounded*, with those of the independent variable. Researchers must be able to control confounding variables if they are to conclude that the independent variable and dependent variable are causally related.

Dependent variables in behavioral and social science research are frequently measured by instruments that were developed to assess constructs such as intelligence, extraversion, or test anxiety. Researchers are obligated to describe the *reliability* and the *validity* of such instruments in the method sections of published reports. A **reliable** instrument is one that produces consistent scores from one administration to another, whereas a **valid** instrument is one that accurately measures the construct it was designed to measure. Please note that reliability and validity are related in the sense that a valid measure must also be a reliable measure. After all, an instrument that does not yield consistent results (is not reliable) can not be considered accurate (valid).

However, an instrument need not be valid to be reliable. A watch that is consistently 10 minutes fast is reliable but is hardly a valid (accurate) measure of the time of day.

> Introduction to Hypothesis Testing

The purpose of research in the behavioral and social sciences is to discover relationships between variables, and the process that accomplishes this purpose is called **hypothesis testing**. A hypothesis is a formal statement about a relationship between variables that exists in some population(s) of interest. Hypothesis testing, then, is the process of making an inference (drawing a conclusion) about variable relationships in populations based on evidence observed in samples that are representative of those populations.

When testing hypotheses, researchers are obligated to describe their independent and dependent variables with sufficient precision and clarity. These descriptions are so important they have a special name: operational definitions. An **operational definition** of a variable is always expressed in terms of the procedures (operations) used to manipulate or measure the variable.

Conducting Experiments to Control for Confounding Variables

Correlational studies are one way to test a hypothesis. The term **correlation** refers to an association between at least two, usually interval, variables. A correlational study, then, is any study in which the correlation between at least two variables is assessed. However, it is important to note that the variables analyzed in a correlational study are *observed* rather than *manipulated*—that is, the researcher simply measures the variables as they exist. Experiments are preferred over correlations.

In a true **experiment**, the effects of most potentially confounding variables are controlled by randomly assigning participants to conditions. As long as the groups of participants are sufficiently large, random assignment virtually guarantees that the groups are equivalent before the independent variable is manipulated. The use of random assignment thus enables the researcher to more confidently conclude that her manipulation of the independent variable *caused* any observed differences in the dependent variable.

Between-Groups Design versus Within-Groups Design

Experiments may be broadly categorized as either between-groups research designs or within-groups research designs. In an experiment with a **between-groups research design**, each participant is randomly assigned to one and only one condition (level or combination of levels of the independent variable).

An experiment with a **within-groups research design** requires each participant experience all the conditions of the study. These designs are often used with naturally occurring events where we observe the same people over time or before and after an event.

STUDY QUESTIONS

1. The two branches of statistics are _____ and _____.
   a. theoretical statistics; applied statistics
   b. research design; data analysis
   c. numerical methods; graphical methods
   d. descriptive statistics; inferential statistics

2. Social and behavioral scientists use _____ statistics to organize, summarize, and communicate a group of numerical observations.
   a. theoretical
   b. inferential
   c. descriptive
   d. applied

3. In _____ statistics, sample data are used to make general estimates about the larger population.
   a. inferential
   b. theoretical
   c. descriptive
   d. applied

4. The _____ includes all possible observations of interest to a researcher, whereas the observations available for study comprise the _____.
   a. sample; population
   b. population; sample
   c. experimental group; control group
   d. control group; experimental group

5. The term **variable** refers to a:
   a. physical, attitudinal, or behavioral characteristic that can take on different values.
   b. number or label assigned to an observation according to a rule or system.
   c. single value that summarizes and describes a sample of data values.
   d. numerical value assigned to an observation.

6. A _____ has an infinite number of possible values.
   a. discrete observation
   b. continuous observation
   c. construct
   d. nominal variable

7. The values of a(n) _____ variable are names or categories.
   a. nominal
   b. ordinal
   c. interval
   d. ratio

8. Which one of the following is a measurement of a **nominal variable**?
   a. reaction time of an adult male measured before and after drinking an ounce of alcohol
   b. a high school senior's first, second, and third choice of colleges to attend
   c. classification of psychiatric patients as either "neurotic" or "psychotic"
   d. estimation of the number of red blood cells in a laboratory sample

9. Which one of the following is an **ordinal variable**?
   a. noon temperature in Boston measured in degrees Fahrenheit
   b. number of first-year college students enrolled at University X
   c. number of stocks sold on the New York Stock Exchange on a given day
   d. military rank from private to four-star general

10. Which one of the following is an **interval variable** but *not* a **ratio variable**?
    a. height (in inches or centimeters)
    b. weight (in pounds or kilograms)
    c. age (in years or days)
    d. temperature (°F or °C)

11. Which one of the following is a **ratio variable**?
    a. the number of times a laboratory monkey presses a bar in an experimental chamber during a one-hour period
    b. the temperature in degrees Celsius of a hospital patient
    c. a driver's order of finish in an automobile race
    d. a patient's rating of his own anxiety level on a scale in which 10 represents "low anxiety" and 100 represents "extreme anxiety"

12. The widely used computer program SPSS refers to _____ variables as scale variables, probably because measures of these variables may be analyzed using the same statistical procedures.
    a. nominal and ordinal
    b. ordinal and interval
    c. interval and ratio
    d. ordinal, interval, and ratio

13. Match each term on the left with a description on the right. (A description may be used more than once.)
    a._____ nominal variable   1. may be discrete or continuous
    b._____ ordinal variable   2. may only be discrete
    c._____ interval variable   3. may only be continuous
    d._____ ratio variable   4. may be neither discrete nor continuous

14. A researcher studying eye color and sun sensitivity examines people with blue eyes, green eyes, and brown eyes. How many levels does the variable of eye color have?
    a. one
    b. two
    c. three
    d. unable to determine

15. An educational psychologist is interested in whether performance on an achievement test is affected by classroom conditions. Accordingly, she administers the test to one group of students in a noisy environment and to another group of students in a quiet environment. Which of the following is the independent variable in this proposed study?
    a. intelligence
    b. achievement test score
    c. classroom conditions
    d. the gender of the student

16. In a certain study, participants in an experimental condition received an injection of the hormone epinephrine (adrenalin) whereas control-group participants received a placebo. Half the participants who received epinephrine were told that the treatment was a vitamin supplement and half were told the truth. Later, each participant was instructed to wait in a room with an individual who, unknown to the participant, was a confederate of the experimenter ("stooge"). Within a few minutes, the stooge began behaving according to a script—either in an obviously euphoric manner or an obviously angry manner. In this study, the dependent variable is:
    a. not described.
    b. the injection (epinephrine vs. placebo).
    c. the behavior of the stooge (angry vs. euphoric).
    d. whether the participant was told the truth or not.

17. A(n) _____ variable is any variable that systematically varies with the independent variable and makes it impossible to determine the cause of any observed changes in the dependent variable.
    a. confounding
    b. extraneous
    c. operational
    d. moderator

18. In a study of the effect of manipulations of variable M on variable N, _____ is (are) the dependent variable(s).
    a. variable M
    b. variable N
    c. both variable M and variable N
    d. neither variable M nor variable N

19. A(n) _____ scale or instrument is one that is consistent.
    a. operationally defined
    b. reliable
    c. valid
    d. ratio

20. A(n) _____ scale or instrument is one that measures what it was intended to measure.
    a. operationally defined
    b. reliable
    c. valid
    d. ratio

21. A test that is:
    a. not reliable can not be valid.
    b. not valid can not be reliable.
    c. valid is also reliable.
    d. reliable is also valid.

22. The term _____ refers to the process of drawing conclusions about whether a particular relation between variables is supported by the evidence.
    a. hypothesis testing
    b. sampling
    c. validity
    d. reliability

23. An **operational definition** of a variable is a definition of the variable in terms of:
    a. its relationship to the independent and dependent variables.
    b. the procedures or operations used to measure or manipulate the variable.
    c. whether it is being used as the independent variable or the dependent variable.
    d. the network of theoretical constructs to which the variable is related.

24. In a study of the effectiveness of a certain new therapy for depression, 30 depressed individuals are randomly assigned to receive the new therapy and 30 other depressed persons are randomly assigned to receive a standard therapy for depression. After six months of therapy, the Beck Depression Inventory and structured interviews are used to assess each individual. Which one of the following indicates that this study is an **experiment**?
    a. random assignment of participants to conditions
    b. exposing the two groups to different forms of therapy
    c. the use of a double-blind procedure to control confounding variables
    d. This study is not an experiment.

25. The use of **random assignment** of participants to different conditions enables an investigator to:
    a. generalize the results of a study to other settings and populations.
    b. measure the relationship between two naturally-occurring variables.
    c. control for the effects of other variables that might affect the dependent variable.
    d. separate the actual effects of a treatment from belief in the effect of the treatment.

26. A researcher proposed to conduct an experiment to determine whether playing the Scrabble board game improves vocabulary. She suspected that individuals with higher IQs, more education, and higher incomes might have more extensive vocabularies. In this proposed study, IQ, education level, and income are _____ variables.
    a. dependent
    b. potentially confounding
    c. independent
    d. archival

27. A **correlation** is:
    a. used to assess a cause-effect relationship between variables.
    b. an association between two or more, usually interval, variables.
    c. an association between two or more variables, both of which have been manipulated.
    d. an association between two or more variables, only one of which has been manipulated.

28. A _____ is one in which participants experience only one level of the independent variable.
    a. between-groups research design
    b. within-groups research design
    c. counterbalanced design
    d. correlational design

29. Which of the following is (are) correct regarding **within-groups research designs**?
    a. Each participant experiences only one condition of the experiment.
    b. Each participant experiences all the conditions of the experiment.
    c. Within-groups designs are far more common than between-groups designs.
    d. Random assignment is frequently used to control order (e.g., practice) effects.

ANSWERS TO CHAPTER 1 STUDY QUESTIONS

Question Number	Correct Answer	Question Number	Correct Answer
1	d, p. 3	14	c, p. 7
2	c, p. 3	15	c, pp. 7–8
3	a, p. 3	16	a, p. 8
4	b, p. 3	17	a, p. 8
5	a, p. 4	18	b, p. 8
6	b, p. 4	19	b, p. 9
7	a, p. 5	20	c, p. 9
8	c, p. 5	21	a, pp. 9–10
9	d, p. 5	22	a, p. 10
10	d, p. 5 (Note that the Fahrenheit and Celsius scales do not include a true zero—that is, both scales include sub-zero values.)	23	b, p. 12
		24	a, p. 12
		25	c, p. 12
		26	b, p. 8, pp. 12–13
		27	b, p. 14
11	a, p. 5	28	a, p. 13
12	c, p. 6	29	b, p. 13
13	a (2), b (2), c (1), d (1) p. 6		

Frequency Distributions

LEARNING OBJECTIVES

After studying this chapter, you should be able to:

1. Define each of the following terms and provide examples that are not in the text: *raw scores, frequency distribution, frequency table, grouped frequency table, histogram, frequency polygon, normal distribution, skewed distribution, positively skewed data, floor effect, negatively skewed data, ceiling effect.*

2. Explain how a *frequency table, grouped frequency table, histogram,* and *frequency polygon* are constructed and describe the kinds of data distributions for which each of these techniques would be appropriate.

3. Compare and contrast *normal* and *nonnormal*, or skewed, distributions.

4. Discuss the relation between *positively* and *negatively skewed* data distributions and the presence of *floor* and *ceiling effects.*

CHAPTER REVIEW

> **Frequency Distributions**

Descriptive statistics include tabular, graphical, and statistical methods of organizing and summarizing the information contained in samples of data. Tables and graphs offer visually appealing methods of organizing distributions of data and four are discussed in your text: frequency tables, grouped frequency tables, frequency histograms, and frequency polygons. A **frequency table** lists scores in one column and the frequencies with which each score was observed in the next column. A **grouped frequency table** is used to organize scores into intervals when the range of scores is too large to list each one. Frequency histograms and **polygons** are graphs used to display scores that have been organized into frequency or grouped frequency tables. Review your text for the steps to make a frequency table, grouped frequency table, histogram or polygon.

Frequency tables are used to organize and summarize data from any scale of measurement as long as the values are discrete and the range is limited. However, for interval and ratio data that represent values of continuous variables, a grouped frequency distribution is usually required.

Frequencies may also be displayed in a variant of a bar chart called a **histogram**. A histogram of math anxiety ratings looks like this:

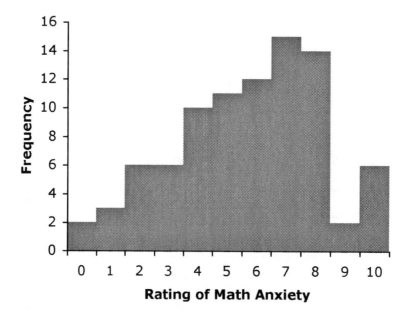

The frequency of each rating is represented by the height of the bar above that rating. The bars in a histogram are usually displayed with no gaps between them. There are no gaps between adjacent ratings because most, if not all, psychological variables that are measured on an interval or ratio scale are thought to have an underlying distribution that is continuous. It is only the limits of the measuring instrument that make the values appear to be discrete.

> Shapes of Distributions

Normal Distributions

The normal, or "bell," curve is perhaps the most famous (or infamous) symbol in statistics. Its use in statistical analysis is demonstrated by noting that the values of most variables of interest to behavioral and social scientists are distributed in a manner that may be well-approximated by a normal curve. There are many normal curves. However, all normal curves share the following characteristics.

- *unimodal*: a single mode or peak
- *symmetric*: the half of the distribution to the left of the center is the mirror image of the half to the right of center
- *bell-shaped*: the shape follows in part from the first two properties, but there are other shapes that are unimodal and symmetric (e.g., an equilateral triangle has a single peak, is symmetric about the center, but is clearly not bell-shaped)
- *central tendency convergence*: all methods for capturing what is common or "typical" are located at the same point along the horizontal axis of a normal curve

Please note that the properties listed above are also descriptive of distributions that are not exactly normal in shape. This fact serves as a useful reminder that the normal curve is a mathematical function as opposed to a distribution of actual measurements. That's why we should always be careful to say that the normal curve is *well-approximated* by many distributions of various measures of interest to scientists from a variety of disciplines.

Skewed Distributions

Skewness refers to how the frequencies of the scores are distributed along the horizontal axis. Distributions are **positively skewed** if most of the scores are bunched at the low end of the range of scores with progressively fewer scores falling near the high end. The long "tail" extends to the *right*.

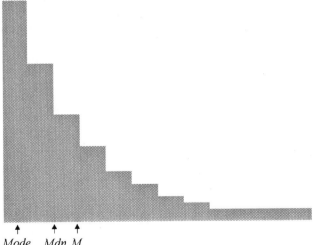

Mode Mdn M

Distributions may be *positively skewed* because of a **floor effect.** A floor effect occurs when most of the scores "pile up" at the lower end of the distribution; because of the presence of a lower limit or "floor."

Distributions that are **negatively skewed** extend in the opposite direction; that is, most of the scores are bunched at the high end of the range, with the tail extending to the *left*.

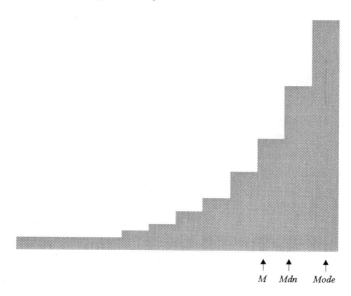

Distributions may be *negatively skewed* because of a **ceiling effect**. A ceiling effect occurs when most of the scores are clustered at the high end of the distribution because of the presence of an upper limit or "ceiling."

STUDY QUESTIONS

1. Which of the following may be displayed in a **frequency table?**
   a. the different values of a variable
   b. the number of times each variable value was chosen by a participant
   c. a variable value with a frequency of zero (i.e., no scores match this value)
   d. All the answers are correct.

2. A frequency table may be used to describe _____ data.
   a. nominal
   b. ordinal
   c. interval or ratio
   d. All the answers are correct.

3. A **grouped frequency table** is required when working with measures of a(n) _____ variable.
   a. continuous
   b. interval or ratio
   c. ordinal or nominal
   d. All the answers are correct.

4. A **histogram** may be constructed from:
   a. any sample of data as long as there are at least two scores for each individual.
   b. a frequency table but not a grouped frequency table.
   c. a grouped frequency table but not a frequency table.
   d. either a frequency table or a grouped frequency table.

5. A **frequency polygon** is a type of _____.
   a. table
   b. line graph
   c. bar graph
   d. descriptive statistic

6. Which of the following describe(s) a **normal distribution**?
   a. unimodal, symmetrical, and bell–shaped
   b. bimodal, symmetrical, and bell–shaped
   c. unimodal, asymmetrical, and positively skewed
   d. unimodal, asymmetrical, and negatively skewed

7. The values of most variables that are of interest to researchers in the social and behavioral sciences have a _____ distribution.
   a. normal
   b. positively skewed
   c. negatively skewed
   d. bimodal

8. A distribution that has many low scores and trails off as it extends to higher values is:
   a. normal.
   b. skewed.
   c. negatively skewed.
   d. positively skewed.

9. When some kind of constraint prevents low values of a variable from being observed, this is called a:
   a. normal effect.
   b. floor effect.
   c. ceiling effect.
   d. skew effect.

10. A _____ distribution is one in which most of the scores are at the high end of the scale with relatively few scores in the middle and lower end.
    a. platykurtic
    b. positively skewed
    c. negatively skewed
    d. mesokurtic

11. The tail of a _____ distribution extends to the left.
    a. normal
    b. negatively skewed
    c. positively skewed
    d. mesokurtic

12. The presence of a **ceiling effect** is usually indicated by a _____ distribution of scores.
    a. positively skewed
    b. negatively skewed
    c. symmetric and unimodal
    d. rectangular

ANSWERS TO CHAPTER 2 STUDY QUESTIONS

Question Number	Correct Answer	Question Number	Correct Answer
1	d, pp. 23–26	4	d, p. 29
2	d, pp. 23–26	5	b, p. 31
3	a, p. 26 (Not all interval or ratio data are measurements of a continuous variable. For example, number of siblings or number of times voted in the last five years are discrete variables, and the limited range of values of these variables would be displayed in a frequency table.)	6	a, p. 34
		7	a, p. 34
		8	d, p. 34
		9	b, p. 34
		10	c, p. 35
		11	b, p. 35
		12	b, p. 35

CHAPTER 3

Visual Displays of Data

CHAPTER OUTLINE

How to Mislead with Graphs
- "The Most Misleading Graph Ever Published"
- Techniques for Misleading with Graphs

Common Types of Graphs
- Scatterplots
- Line Graphs
- Bar Graphs
- Pictorial Graphs
- Pie Charts

How to Build a Graph
- Choosing the Type of Graph Based on Variables
- How to Read a Graph
- Guidelines for Creating the Perfect Graph
- The Future of Graphs

LEARNING OBJECTIVES

After studying this chapter, you should be able to:

1. Define each of the following terms and provide examples that are not in the text: *scatterplot, linear relation, nonlinear relation, line graph, time plot or time series plot, bar graph, Pareto chart, pictorial graph, pie chart, chartjunk, Moiré vibrations, grids, ducks.*

2. Discuss how graphs are used to inform and to mislead. Include in your discussion a brief description of each of the four "lies" depicted in "the most misleading graph ever published."

3. Describe the kinds of variable relationships that are appropriately displayed in scatterplots, line graphs (including time series plots), and bar graphs (including Pareto charts). Discuss the limitations of pictorial graphs and pie charts.

4. Discuss the importance of graphing literacy as it relates to recent developments in computer technology and the increasing access to information associated with these developments. Include in your discussion an identification and brief description of the 6 ways in which

graphs may be used inappropriately to distort information and deceive consumers of that information. Wrap up your discussion with a brief description of some recent advances in graphing tools, including interactive graphs.

CHAPTER REVIEW

> How to Mislead with Graphs

An ability to inform, or even persuade, with pictorial descriptions of information is becoming increasingly important as advances in computer technology enable access to information that was almost unfathomable just a few decades ago. Viewed in this context, it is very important that students in the behavioral sciences become critical consumers of that information as they acquire the skills to create effective graphs and interpret visual displays of data encountered routinely in the popular media and the professional literature.

A few basics should establish a solid foundation as you pursue the goal of graphic literacy. A useful starting point is to examine a graph that Michael Friendly of York University labeled "**the most misleading graph ever published**." The graph appeared on the cover of the December 7, 2000 edition of the *Ithaca Times* and is reproduced in Figure 3-3 on p. 45 in your text. The graph/cover purports to relate the rising cost of an education at Cornell University to changes in the quality of that education but does so in an alarmingly misleading fashion. You should review the complete discussion in the text of the deceptions and distortions in the graph.

Graphic literacy is a critical thinking skill. Remember also that the details of a graph's appearance are determined by you, the graph's creator. There are default choices built into graphics software programs, but it is your responsibility to override those defaults as you build your graph with its major purpose in mind: to clearly and effectively depict the relations between variables. During the construction of a graph, each seemingly trivial decision point is an opportunity to engage rather than dupe, enlighten rather than mislead. The graph that you create says something about you. What would you like that message to be?

Techniques for Misleading with Graphs

1. *The false face validity lie.* This method of deception occurs when the operational definition of a variable lacks face validity—that is, the way the variable is measured or manipulated does not appear (on its "face") to be an honest attempt to capture the essence of the variable's conceptual (i.e., more abstract, or general) definition.

2. *The biased scale lie.* A biased scale is one that elicits mostly favorable or unfavorable responses and thereby results in a skewed distribution. For example, the following 5-point scale will elicit mostly favorable responses because the scale's anchors are mostly positive adjectives.

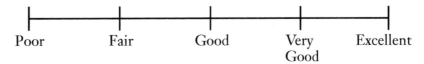

Poor   Fair   Good   Very   Excellent
                                          Good

3. *The sneaky sample lie.* Here, the culprit is a sample that is self-selected. Any method of participant selection that is not random will result in a biased sample, and self-selected samples are the most biased of all. The most common example of a self-selected sample is one that is composed of individuals who complete a survey or questionnaire because they have strong feelings about the topic.

4. *The extrapolation lie.* Extrapolation occurs when an observed relation between variables is assumed to extend beyond the range of data in the sample. It is quite possible that a relation apparent in a sample of data may not hold for values beyond this observed range. Thus, like interpolation, extrapolation is speculative and potentially deceptive. It is rarely, if ever, advisable to generalize beyond the range of data within a sample.

5. *The inaccurate values lie.* This error is most likely to occur when pictures or other symbols are used to represent data values. Figure 3-4 on p. 47 in the text is an example of how the proportional changes in the dimensions of the picture-graphic misrepresent the proportional changes in the values of the variable.

6. *The outright lie.* Given the pressure to "publish or perish" that exists in many large research universities, it is hardly surprising that the history of science is rife with cases of outright data fabrication. Recently, Korean scientist Hwang Woo Suk authored a paper published in *Science* in which he claimed to have extracted stem cells from human embryos cloned in his lab. He resigned from Seoul National University after colleagues told university officials that he had falsified the data.

> Common Types of Graphs

The histograms and polygons introduced in Chapter 2 are graphic displays of the frequencies of single variables measured on either an interval or ratio scale. As such, they are used most frequently during the initial steps of data analysis to identify patterns in raw data and are very rarely encountered in either the popular media or the professional literature. The histograms and polygons that appear in the published literature are most likely to be displays of the distributions of demographic characteristics of research participants such as age, income, or years of formal education. The results sections of published articles are far more likely to include graphs that depict the relation between two or more variables. These multivariable graphs include *scatterplots, line graphs, bar graphs*, and (less frequently) *pictorial graphs* and *pie charts*.

A **scatterplot** is used to portray the relation between two variables that are measured on an interval or ratio scale. The variable designated as the "X" variable is conceptualized as the *independent variable* (the variable whose values are used to predict the values of the other variable), and the horizontal (X) axis of the scatterplot should be titled with the name of the independent variable. The other variable, designated as "Variable Y," is the *dependent variable* (the variable whose values may be predicted by, and thus depend on, those of the independent variable), and the title of the vertical (Y) axis should be the name of the dependent variable. Each pair of scores for a given participant is plotted as a single point at the intersection of the score on the independent variable and the score on the dependent variable.

Although scatterplots sometimes appear in research articles, they are constructed primarily to determine whether there is a **linear relation** between the variables. A linear relation is observed if the points in a scatterplot may be approximated by a straight line as in the scatterplot on the previous page. If the relation appears to be linear, the statistical methods described in Chapters 13 (correlation) and 14 (regression) may be applied to determine the degree to which the variables are linearly related (correlation) and to predict values of the dependent variable from values of the independent variable (regression). A scatterplot will also reveal a **nonlinear relation** between variables, such as the relation between arousal and performance described by the Yerkes-Dodson law.

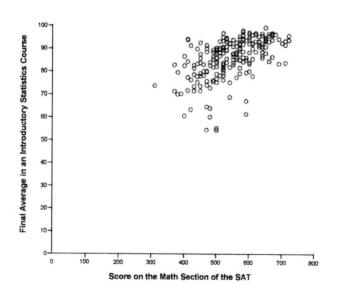

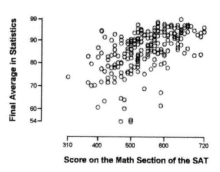

Like a scatterplot, a **line graph** depicts the relation between variables measured on an interval or ratio scale. A key difference, of course, is that a line graph features a continuous line to represent changes in the dependent variable as a function of changes in the independent variable. Fitting a line to the points in a scatterplot transforms the scatterplot into a kind of line graph that may be used to predict values of the dependent variable from values of the independent variable. However, the line graphs that appear in research articles generally depict changes in the dependent variable over time (a **time-series plot**) or some other continuously distributed interval or ratio variable such as temperature. A line graph that figures prominently in the history of psychology is the "forgetting curve" constructed from data recorded by Hermann Ebbinghaus, a nineteenth-century experimental psychologist who used himself as his experimental subject. The graph can be seen below.

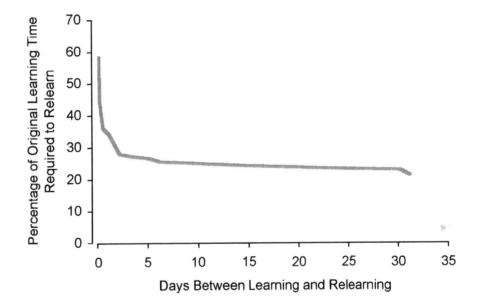

Bar graphs are most commonly used to display the relation between a dependent variable measured on an interval or ratio scale and an independent variable measured on a nominal scale. The height of each bar corresponds to a numeric assessment for the group whose name (a nominal value of the independent variable) appears just beneath the bar. The bar graph on the following page compares the mean (a measure of "average") departure times for drivers exiting their parking spaces under two conditions: alone ("No Intruder") and in the presence of a waiting driver ("Intruder").

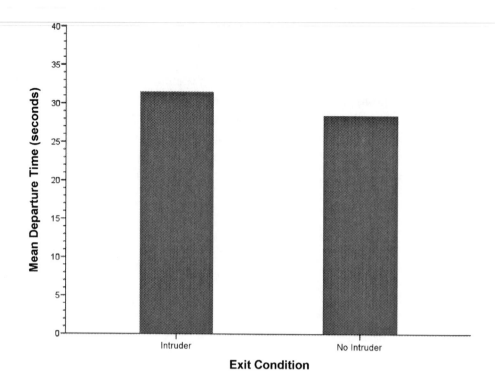

The versatility of bar graphs is illustrated by **Pareto charts,** bar graphs in which the bars are arranged in order with the highest bar on the left and the lowest bar on the right. Pareto charts are used when there are several categories of an independent variable. The world's 11 most populous countries (http://www.nationmaster.com/) are arranged in alphabetical order in the bar graph below on the left. The Pareto chart on the right facilitates a more direct comparison by ordering the countries according to population (see also Figure 3-9 on p. 53 in the text).

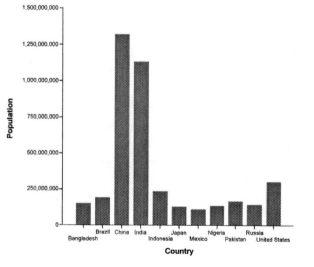

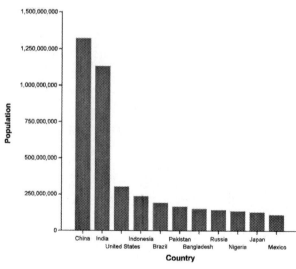

Pictorial graphs and pie charts appear in the popular media but should not be used to present research results. As its name suggests, a **pictorial graph** uses a picture or symbol instead of a bar to indicate the value of the dependent variable for each category of the independent variable. A **pie chart** is divided into slices that represent the categories of a single independent variable. The area of each slice represents the proportion, or percentage of cases in that category. Because proportions and percentages may be more clearly presented in a bar graph, pie charts are indeed passé.

> How to Build a Graph

Choosing the Type of Graph Based on Variables

The choice of graphical display depends most basically on its purpose. If the purpose of the graph is to display a frequency distribution, then the choice is between a bar graph and a histogram or frequency polygon. Use a bar graph if the variable is measured on a nominal or ordinal scale, and a histogram or polygon if the variable is measured on an interval or ratio scale. If the purpose of the graph is to display the relation between an independent variable and a dependent variable, then the choice depends on the type of independent variable—that is, the scale on which the independent variable is measured. (We are assuming that the dependent variable is measured on an interval or ratio scale. Methods of analysis used when the dependent variable is measured on a nominal or ordinal scale are discussed in Chapter 15.) If the independent variable is measured on an interval or ratio scale, then the appropriate display is a scatterplot or a line graph. If the independent variable is measured on a nominal scale, then a bar graph is used to display the relation between the variables. A bar graph can accommodate a second, or even a third, independent variable.

How to Read a Graph

When reading a graph, begin by identifying the independent and dependent variables. Graphs that depict the relationship between two variables tell us something about how one variable (the independent variable) influences another variable (the dependent or outcome variable). In addition to identifying these variables, consider how they were assessed, what scores were possible, and the level of measurement of each variable. All this information is important in determining whether the kind of graph presented is appropriate and "readable."

Guidelines for Creating the Perfect Graph

Two general guidelines to keep in mind as you prepare to create a graph are:

1. The terms that appear in the graph (e.g., the names of the independent and dependent variables, the terms used to label the symbols in the

figure legend, and any terms in the figure caption) should match those used in the text of your report.

2. The graph should be a clearly presented, complete representation of the relation between the variables displayed therein. If the reader has to return to the text to understand your graph, then you have not met this basic requirement.

Default options in computer software are likely to place *chartjunk* in your graph. **Chartjunk** is a term coined by Edward Tufte that refers to "any unnecessary information or feature in a graph that detracts from a viewer's ability to understand the data." Examples of chartjunk include *moiré vibrations*, *grids*, and *ducks*. **Moiré vibrations** are "any of the patterns that computers provide as options to fill in bars" (text page 58). Grids and at least one duck are included among the default options displayed in the graph on the left below. The **grids** are the thin lines extending horizontally across the graph, whereas the *duck* is the dark gray shadows outlining the symbols and the lines connecting them. More generally, a **duck** is any feature added to the graph that is intended to "dress up" the data but which more often obscures it. Additional examples of graphical ducks include the use of "fancy fonts" and "cutesy pictures." The version of the graph on the right shows these elements removed

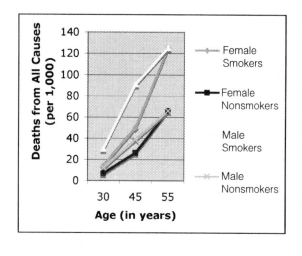
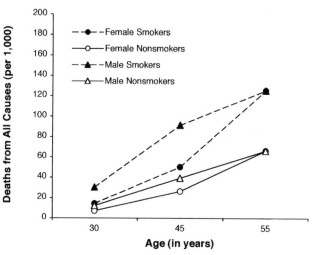

If a graph is worth constructing, then the following guidelines should be observed:

- Select a graph based on the types of variables you have.
- Follow the basic rules of graph construction.
- Make sure that the graph effectively addresses your hypothesis.
- Include all of the data that you included in your analysis.
- Include only the independent and dependent variables in your graph.
- If the graph requires a key to symbols (figure legend), make sure that it is easy to interpret.

- Construct a "clean" graph that communicates the message in your data in an orderly, efficient manner, without resort to "gimmicks" such as ducks and other forms of chartjunk.
- Assume responsibility for the graphs that you create.

The Future of Graphs

The most striking advances in the visual display of information take advantage of the user's ability to interact with digital media, including links on Web pages that grant access to information at multiple levels.

Forensic graphing and the use of graphs to monitor therapy represent the application of more standard graphic techniques to practical problems. Clinical psychologists and other therapists can enlist the help of standard line graphs to track clients' rates of improvement over time against expected rates of improvement for clients with particular profiles (see Figure 3-16, p. 60 in the text).

STUDY QUESTIONS

1. Which of the following statements regarding graphs is most clearly false?
   a. The purpose of a graph is to reveal and clarify relations between variables.
   b. A graph can sometimes reveal more about the person creating the graph than it does about the data it represents.
   c. Once a particular type of graph is selected, details related to the appearance of the graph are determined by software.
   d. It is possible to construct a graph that is deliberately misleading.

2. Which of the following statements regarding rules for the construction of graphic displays of data is most accurate?
   a. There are no rules. It is up to the graph creator to decide how to construct the graph.
   b. Rules for the construction of graphs have been rendered obsolete by graphic software.
   c. There are conventional rules, and failing to adhere to them frequently results in misleading graphs or graphs that obscure information that may be of vital importance.
   d. The rules vary markedly from one academic field to another, so it would be incorrect to say that there are conventional rules that apply across disciplines.

3. Of the 11 sophisticated techniques for lying with statistics and graphs, which one refers to the use of an operational definition of a variable that doesn't represent the variable's conceptual definition (e.g., using the frequency or duration of shouting as an operational definition of *aggression*)?
   a. the biased scale lie
   b. the false face validity lie
   c. the false impression lie
   d. the sneaky sample lie

4. Korean scientist Hwang Woo Suk's confession that he fabricated much of the data, statistics, and graphs in his highly publicized cloning and stem cell research is a relatively recent example of a technique of deceiving with statistics and graphs called the _____ lie.
   a. outright
   b. false impression
   c. extrapolation
   d. inaccurate values

5. What do *scatterplots*, *line graphs*, and *bar graphs* have in common?
   a. They are all used to display the relation between two or more variables.
   b. They are all used to display the frequency distribution of a single variable.
   c. They are all used to display the frequency distributions of two or more variables.
   d. They are examples of older graphic displays that have been rendered obsolete by modern computer software.

6. A _____ is a graph that depicts the relation between two scale variables.
   a. pie chart
   b. bar graph
   c. histogram
   d. scatterplot

7. In a **scatterplot**, the variable doing the predicting is called the _____ variable.
   a. dependent
   b. independent
   c. interval
   d. moderator

8. An important feature of a scatterplot is its ability to identify:
   a. a causal relation between variables.
   b. confounding variables.
   c. extraneous variables.
   d. linear and nonlinear relations.

9. There is a _____ relation between two variables when the pattern of points in a scatterplot roughly resembles a straight line.
   a. positive
   b. linear
   c. nonlinear
   d. negative

10. A _____ may used to represent change in a(n) _____ variable over time.
    a. line graph; scale
    b. line graph; nominal
    c. bar graph; scale
    d. bar graph; nominal

11. Which of the following should be used to predict job performance from an applicant's score on a vocational aptitude test?
    a. a scatterplot with a line of best fit
    b. a time-series plot
    c. a bar graph with applicants' aptitude scores measured on the horizontal axis
    d. a bar graph with applicants' job performance measured on the horizontal axis

12. In a **time series plot**, the horizontal axis is labeled with the name of the _____ variable; the values of this variable are _____.
    a. independent; measures of a variable that changes over time
    b. dependent; measures of a variable that changes over time
    c. independent; increments of time
    d. dependent; increments of time

13. In a **bar graph** depicting the relation between two variables, the height of each bar typically represents the:
    a. median score on the dependent variable.
    b. average score on the dependent variable.
    c. level of the independent variable.
    d. frequency of responses.

14. A **Pareto chart** is a type of _____ that orders the categories of an independent variable along the horizontal axis for easier comparisons.
    a. bar graph
    b. line graph
    c. pictorial graph
    d. scatterplot

15. Identify the error, if there is one, in the graph below.

**Effect of Sexual Harassment Status on Female Navy Officers'
Intentions to Stay in the Navy**

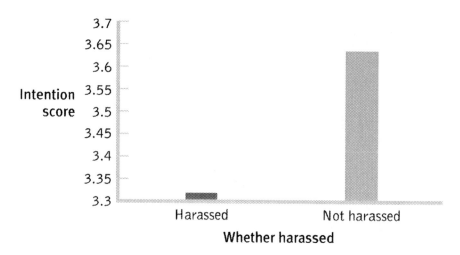

a. The graph is correct as is.
b. The vertical axis is too busy.
c. The vertical axis does not begin at zero.
d. The horizontal axis is labeled incorrectly.

16. Which one of the following uses a picture or symbol to represent the value of the dependent variable for each level of the independent variable?
a. Pareto chart
b. bar graph
c. pie chart
d. pictorial graph

17. Which one of the following is a graph in the shape of a circle?
a. pie chart
b. pictorial graph
c. Pareto chart
d. Moiré display

18. Suppose that a **pie chart** is constructed to represent responses to a survey question. The size of each slice in the chart represents the:
a. mean score for each category of participants.
b. median score for each category of participants.
c. proportion or percentage of individuals choosing each response.
d. proportion of variability in the dependent variable that is explained by the independent variable.

19. Which one of the following graphs most effectively depicts the relation between an interval variable and a nominal variable?
    a. pictorial graph
    b. pie chart
    c. bar graph
    d. line graph

20. Match the description of variables in the left column with the appropriate graph from the right column. (A graph may be appropriate for more than one description of variables.)
    a. _____ one scale variable (with frequencies)   1. bar graph
    b. _____ one scale independent variable and   2. line graph or scatterplot
       one interval dependent variable   3. histogram or polygon
    c. _____ one nominal independent variable and   4. pie chart
       one scale dependent variable
    d. _____ two or more nominal independent variables
       and one scale dependent variable

21. *Histograms* and *polygons* are:
    a. frequently presented in the results sections of published research articles.
    b. commonly used to display the relation between two or more variables.
    c. frequently presented in media accounts of scientific research.
    d. used to display frequency distributions.

22. T F   A graph should use the same terms that were used in the body of the paper.

23. Tufte (2001/2006) coined the term _____ to refer to any unnecessary information or feature in a graph that detracts from a viewer's ability to understand the data.
    a. chartjunk
    b. Moiré vibrations
    c. ducks
    d. grids

24. T F   **Moiré vibrations** are background patterns on which the data representations, such as bars, are superimposed.

25. Graphical **ducks**:
    a. refer to any of the patterns that computers provide as options to fill in bars.
    b. are symbols or pictures used to represent values of the dependent variable.
    c. are features of the data that have been dressed up to be something other than data.
    d. refer collectively to all the default options that are implemented by graphics software.

ANSWERS TO CHAPTER 3 STUDY QUESTIONS

Question Number	Correct Answer	Question Number	Correct Answer
1	c, theme of chapter, no specific page	12	c, p. 51
		13	b, p. 52
2	c, p. 44	14	a, p. 52
3	b, p. 46	15	c, p. 53–54
4	a, p. 47	16	d, p. 54
5	a, p. 48	17	a, p. 55
6	d, p. 48	18	c, p. 55
7	b, p. 49	19	c, p. 56
8	d, p. 49	20	a (3), b (2), c (1), d (1) [p. 56]
9	b, p. 49 (A linear relation may be positive or negative, but you can't tell which from the description in this question stem.)	21	d, p. 56
		22	T, p. 57
		23	a, p. 57
		24	F, p. 58
10	a, p. 50	25	c, p. 58
11	a, p. 50–51		

Central Tendency and Variability

LEARNING OBJECTIVES

After studying this chapter, you should be able to:

1. Define each of the following terms and provide examples that are not in the text: *central tendency, mean, statistics, parameters, median, mode, unimodal, bimodal, multimodal, outlier, range, standard deviation, deviation from the mean, variance, sum of squares.*

2. Describe the kinds of data distributions for which the *mean, median,* and *mode* would be appropriate (and inappropriate) as measures of *central tendency,* and explain how each of these descriptive statistics are determined from a distribution of raw data.

3. Explain how the *range, variance,* and *standard deviation* are computed, and describe the kinds of data distributions for which the range and standard deviation would be appropriate (and inappropriate) as measures of *variability.*

CHAPTER REVIEW

> **Central Tendency**

So far we've seen that samples of data may be *organized* using tables and graphs. Samples of data may be also be *summarized* by single values called descriptive statistics. Generally, two values are computed to summarize a group of scores: a measure of *central tendency* (or *center*) and a measure of *variability* (or *spread*).

Statistics that measure the **central tendency** of a group of scores are values considered to be *typical* or *representative* of all scores in the group. The *mean*, *median*, and *mode* all measure the center of a group of scores, but each defines "center" differently. The statistic used frequently depends upon the shape of the distribution and the scale of measurement.

Mean, The Arithmetic Average

The mean is probably the most familiar measure of central tendency, although you probably know it as the "average," a relatively general term that can refer to any measure of central tendency. The full name of the mean is the *arithmetic* mean. The arithmetic mean is computed by summing all of the scores and dividing by the number of scores in the group. The formula is presented below in the context of introducing summation notation. The mean is by far the most commonly reported measure of central tendency. However, its use is restricted to variables measured on at least an interval scale. The mean does not have to be one of the scores, or even a *possible* score, in the distribution. Statisticians use the symbol $\overline{X}$ (read "X bar") to represent the mean of a sample of scores, whereas researchers in the social and behavioral sciences are probably more likely to follow the guideline of the American Psychological Association and use an italicized uppercase *M* to represent the sample mean. The Greek letter μ (pronounced "mew" and spelled "mu") is the universal symbol for the mean of a population. When the mean is used [as] a measure of central tendency for a *sample* of scores, it is called a **statistic**, whereas the mean of an entire *population* is called a **parameter**. The same goes for values computed to describe other properties of distributions, such as the measures of variability described below.

Statistical formulas are expressed in *summation notation*, a system of symbols that represent scores, statistics, and the operations used to compute them. For example, the formula for the mean is:

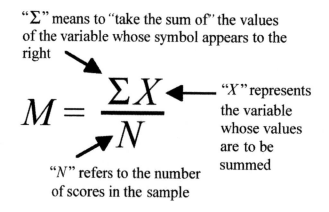

"Σ" means to "take the sum of" the values of the variable whose symbol appears to the right

$$M = \frac{\Sigma X}{N}$$

"X" represents the variable whose values are to be summed

"N" refers to the number of scores in the sample

Median, The Middle Score

The **median** is the *ordinal center* of a distribution, that is, the median is the middle score of a distribution in which the scores have been ranked in order. Thus half of the scores in a distribution are ranked below the median and half are ranked above the median. The symbol for the median is *mdn*.

To determine the median, first arrange the scores in ascending or descending order, and locate the score that has the same number of scores above and below it. If *N* is even, then the median is the arithmetic mean of the two scores in the middle; if *N* is odd, then the median is the score in the middle; that is, no other steps are necessary.

Mode, The Most Common Score

Of the three most frequently used measures of central tendency, the mode is the easiest to determine and the least informative: The **mode** is simply the most frequently occurring score in the sample. In the array of scores below, the mode is 6, because this score was observed two times and no other score occurred more than once. This distribution is said to be **unimodal** because it has just one mode. If no score is observed more than once in a distribution, then there is no mode. If there are two scores that occurred with equal frequency, then the distribution is said to be **bimodal**. If more than two scores are observed with equal frequency, then the distribution is described as **multimodal**. The mode is the *only* measure of central tendency that may be used when the variable is measured on a nominal scale. The mode may also be used when the variable is measured on either an ordinal or equal-interval scale, but is less informative in these instances than either the mean or the median.

How Outliers Affect Measures of Central Tendency

The mean is sensitive to the *interval value*, whereas the median is sensitive only to the *ordinal position*, of each score in a distribution. Consider the following array of scores:

2,   3,   5,   6,   6,   7,   11,   14,   16,   17,   21

If the score "21" is changed to "210," the median remains the same (*mdn* = 7), but the mean is markedly increased (from 9.82 to 27.00). Because the mean is sensitive to the value of each score in a distribution, it will always be "pulled" in the direction of extreme scores, or **outliers**. In contrast, the median is sensitive only to the ordinal position, or rank, of each score and will not be pulled toward outliers. For this reason, the mean is *not* the preferred measure of center for distributions that include outliers.

Which Measure of Central Tendency Is Best?

The measure of central tendency you present is based on the type of data you have (nominal, ordinal, or scale), whether there are outliers in the data, and the story you are trying to tell with the data.

The mean, followed by the median, is the most commonly used measure of central tendency. As noted earlier, the mean is not preferred when the data contain outliers. In that case, the median is typically presented because of its resistance to the effect of outliers. The mode is used with nominal data and to present information about the shape of distributions (as in the case of bimodal distributions). The mode is commonly used to capture situations in which one score/observation clearly leads over others, such as the case of the most popular baby name of 2010.

Your decision about which measure to present is an important one that can lead to accurate and inaccurate (deceptive) interpretations of the data.

> Measures of Variability

Range

A measure of central tendency is usually accompanied by a measure of **variability**, because distributions can be similar with regard to one of these measures but very different with regard to the other. The simplest to determine, but least informative measure of spread is the range. The **range** is computed by simply subtracting the smallest score from the largest. It is a crude measure of variability because it ignores all but the two most extremes scores.

$$range = X_{highest} - X_{lowest}$$

Variance

The most commonly reported measure of variability is the **standard deviation**. This statistic is computed as the square root of the **variance**, a less commonly reported descriptive statistic but one that figures prominently in the calculation of several important inferential statistics. Both statistics measure the deviation of scores from the mean and thus require that the scores in the sample be measured on at least an interval scale. The symbol and definitional formula[1] for the variance is as follows:

$$SD^2 = \frac{\sum(X - M)^2}{N}$$

At the heart of the formulas for computing the variance and the standard deviation is the **sum of squares (SS)**, a foundational concept for much of descrip-

---

[1] As the name suggests, a *definitional formula* for a statistic is closely related to its definition and thus facilitates learning to calculate, interpret, and use the statistic. Prior to the widespread availability of computing devices, statisticians used a computational formula to compute the variance and thereby avoided the rounding error that sometimes occurred when the mean was subtracted from each score.

tive and inferential statistics. As you can see from the following formulas, the sum of squares is exactly what its name indicates: the sum of squared deviations of each score from the mean. The variance, then, is computed as the mean of these squared deviation scores:

$$SS = \sum (X - M)^2$$

$$SD^2 = \frac{SS}{N}$$

Following are the steps in computing the variance, using the definitional formula above:

1. Compute the mean.
2. Subtract the mean from each score, then square the difference.
3. Sum the squares that you computed in Step 2.
4. Divide the result of Step 3 by N, the number of scores.

Standard Deviation

The shortcoming of the variance as a descriptive statistic is that it is an average of *squared* deviation scores and thus appears to inflate the spread in a distribution. To obtain a measure of spread that looks more like the unsquared data values themselves, the square root of the variance is taken, and the resulting statistic is called the **standard deviation**. The definitional formula describes the standard deviation as a sort-of-but-not-really "average" deviation score:

$$SD = \sqrt{\frac{\sum (X - M)^2}{N}}$$

Like M and $\overline{X}$, SD^2 and SD are symbols for sample statistics. Following is a table similar to Table 4-2 from p. 85 in the text, showing the symbols for sample statistics and the corresponding symbols for population parameters.

	Sample Statistics	Population Parameters
Mean	$M, \overline{X}$	μ
Variance	SD^2, s^2	σ^2
Standard Deviation	SD, s	σ

STUDY QUESTIONS

1. The _____ is the most commonly used measure of central tendency.
   a. mean
   b. median
   c. mode
   d. range

2. Consider the following sample of scores:
   13, 18, 9, 27, 15, 28, 5, 16, 21, 23, 29, 15, 15
   What is the **mean**?
   a. 18
   b. 13
   c. 15
   d. 16

3. Which of the following is *not* a symbol for the mean?
   a. X
   b. M
   c. $\overline{X}$
   d. μ

4. Complete the analogy: *Population* mean is to _____ as *sample* mean is to _____.
   a. statistic; parameter
   b. parameter; statistic
   c. descriptive statistic; inferential statistic
   d. inferential statistic; descriptive statistic

5. What does the symbol ΣX tell you to do?
   a. Find the sum of the scores in the distribution of the variable X.
   b. Find the mean of the scores in the distribution of the variable X.
   c. Find the square root of the scores in the distribution of the variable X.
   d. Subtract the mean from each of the scores in the distribution of the variable X.

6. The _____ of a group of scores is the score that is greater than half the scores and less than half the scores.
   a. mode
   b. median
   c. mean
   d. None of these answers are correct.

7. Consider the following sample of scores:
   13, 18, 9, 27, 15, 15, 28, 5, 16, 21, 23, 29, 15, 15
   What is the **median**?
   a. 18
   b. 15
   c. 15.5
   d. 16

8. For any group of scores ordered from lowest to highest, the _____ is the value that results when you divide the number of scores by 2 and add 0.5 to the quotient.
   a. mean
   b. median
   c. mode
   d. ordinal position of the median

9. The _____ is the most frequently occurring score in a group of scores.
   a. mean
   b. mode
   c. median
   d. None of these answers are correct.

10. A(n) _____ distribution has more than one mode.
    a. unimodal
    b. bimodal
    c. multimodal
    d. bimodal or multimodal

11. Whether a distribution is called *unimodal, bimodal,* or *multimodal* depends upon the:
    a. thickness of the tails.
    b. number of high points or peaks.
    c. location of the high points or peaks.
    d. range of scores, from lowest to highest.

12. A single frequency polygon that displays the heights of a large representative sample of men and a large representative sample of women would be described as _____.
    a. positively skewed
    b. negatively skewed
    c. unimodal
    d. bimodal

13. A(n) _____ is an extreme score that is either very low or very high in comparison to the other scores in a sample.

14. Consider the following ages of undergraduate students enrolled in a senior seminar on the psychology of aging:
21, 22, 22, 23, 24, 22, 21, 63, 22, 24, 22, 25, 23, 22
Which measure(s) of central tendency is (are) representative of these data?
    a. the mean
    b. the median
    c. the mode
    d. the median and the mode

15. When your data do not indicate a clear preference for one measure of central tendency over another, you should report the:
    a. mean.
    b. median.
    c. mode.
    d. mean, median, and mode.

16. When the data are values of a(n) _____ variable, the mode is the only appropriate measure of central tendency.
    a. interval
    b. nominal
    c. ordinal
    d. None of these answers are correct.

17. Which of the following measures of variability depend(s) on only two scores?
    a. the standard deviation
    b. the variance
    c. the range
    d. the standard deviation and the variance

18. The variance is most closely related to which of the following statistics?
    a. the range
    b. the interquartile range
    c. the median
    d. the standard deviation

19. Because the _____ is based on squared deviation scores (which do not give an at-a-glance sense of how spread out the original raw scores are), it is reported only occasionally as a descriptive statistic.
    a. standard deviation
    b. range
    c. variance
    d. average deviation

20. To compute the **sum of squares** for a sample of scores you would:
    a. sum all of the scores, square the sum, and divide this sum by the number of scores.
    b. square each score, subtract the mean from each squared score, and sum the differences.
    c. subtract the mean from each score, square each difference, and sum the squared differences.
    d. square each score, sum the squared scores, and divide this sum by the number of scores.

21. The _____ is the typical amount by which the scores in a sample vary from the mean.

22. The most commonly used measure of variability is the:
    a. variance.
    b. range.
    c. interquartile range.
    d. standard deviation.

23. Which of the following is a (are) symbol(s) for the sample variance?
    a. s^2 and σ^2
    b. SD^2 and σ^2
    c. s^2 and SD^2
    d. σ^2, s^2, and SD^2

24. Which one of the following is a formula for the variance?
    a. $\sqrt{\dfrac{\Sigma(X-M)^2}{N}}$
    b. $\dfrac{\Sigma(X-M)^2}{N}$
    c. $\Sigma\sqrt{\dfrac{(X-M)^2}{N}}$
    d. $\dfrac{\Sigma(X-M)}{N}$

25. The standard deviation is the:
    a. square of the variance.
    b. square root of the variance.
    c. average deviation score.
    d. sum of squared deviations.

ANSWERS TO CHAPTER 4 STUDY QUESTIONS

Question Number	Correct Answer
1	a, p. 73
2	a, p. 73
3	a, p. 74
4	b, p. 74
5	a, p. 75
6	b, p. 76
7	c, pp. 76–77 (The median is 15.5, the average of the two middle scores: 5, 9, 13, 15, 15, 15, **15, 16**, 18, 21, 23, 27, 28, 29)
8	d, p. 76 (The formula results in the ordered position, or rank, of the median—not the median, itself—for an odd number of scores. When there is an even number of scores, the formula will result in a value that lies midway between the ordered positions of the two middle scores. The average of these two scores is the median.)

Question Number	Correct Answer
9	b, p. 77
10	d, pp. 77–78
11	b, pp. 77–78
12	d, pp. 77–78
13	outlier (p. 78)
14	d, pp. 78–80 (The median and the mode are both 22. The mean is pulled in the direction of the outlier and thus misrepresents the typical student's age.)
15	d, p. 79
16	b, p. 80
17	c, pp. 81–82
18	d, pp. 82–84
19	c, pp. 82–83
20	c, p. 83
21	standard deviation (p. 84)
22	d, p. 84
23	c, p. 84
24	b, p. 84
25	b, p. 84

Sampling and Probability

LEARNING OBJECTIVES

After studying this chapter, you should be able to:

1. Define each of the following terms and provide examples that are not in the text: *generalizability, random sample, convenience sample, volunteer sample, replication, confirmation bias, subjective (or personal) probability, expected relative-frequency probability, trial, outcome, success, control group, experimental group, null hypothesis, research hypothesis, Type I error, Type II error.*

2. Explain the concepts of generalizability and external validity in the context of sampling.

3. Distinguish between *random samples* and *convenience samples*, and explain why it is difficult to obtain a random sample. What are some special concerns with *volunteer samples*?

4. Contrast *random selection* and *random assignment* and explain how a source of random numbers may be used to assign participants to different levels of an independent variable. Include in your discussion an explanation of the importance of *replication* in studies in which random assignment, but not random selection, is used.

5. Distinguish between *subjective* and *expected relative-frequency probability* and explain the concept of independence (or independent trials).

6. Discuss the procedure and logic of hypothesis testing, including the random assignment of participants to *experimental* and *control groups*, the formulation of statements of the *null* and *research hypotheses*, and the possible decisions regarding the null hypothesis that are dictated by the outcome of a study. Be sure to include in your discussion an explanation of *Type I* and *Type II errors*.

CHAPTER REVIEW

> Samples and Their Populations

In Chapter 1 you learned the distinction between a *sample* and a *population*. You also learned that the purpose of *inferential statistics* is to use the information in a sample of data to draw inferences (make general estimates) about a larger population. More specifically, you learned that *statistics* computed for samples of data may be used to estimate the values of corresponding population *parameters*. A researcher is interested in a sample of individuals only to the extent that the sample is representative of the larger population. For example, a researcher who proposes to study a sample of students from William Patterson College in New Jersey will compute sample statistics as reasonable estimates of the corresponding parameters determined for the population of students attending the college. Researchers working at other institutions have the same goal: to study a sample of individuals who are representative of the larger population.

In this chapter, you were introduced to the terms *generalizability* and *external validity* and the importance of studying representative samples. **Generalizability** refers to the extent to which a researcher's findings may be applied to other samples and contexts. If the findings may be generalized from, say, a sample of students attending the University of Iowa to a sample of students attending William Patterson College in New Jersey, then the findings are said to be high in *external validity*.

If the samples are high in external validity and they are representative of their respective populations, then it follows that findings from either study may be generalized to either population. Ideally, all researchers would like to *generalize* their findings as broadly as possible. Thus the goal of a researcher at Institution X is seldom simply to study a sample that is representative of Institution X or to produce findings that may be generalized to Institution Y. More often the goal is to study a sample that is representative of the national population of college and university students. According to this "big picture" scenario, the results of a single representative sample of participants may be generalized to any other sample from any other institution in the nation.

The "big picture" is an ideal founded on a fundamental goal of science: to discover principles (sometimes called "laws") that hold under a wide range of conditions. Not all problems are of a general nature, however. Sometimes the goal is simply to generalize to a more limited population or set of conditions. Either way, the laws of probability enable researchers to make inferences about an entire population from the information provided by a representative sample.

The two general categories of samples discussed in the text are *random samples* and *convenience samples*. A **random sample** is the result of a process that gives every member of the population an equal chance of being selected. Simple random sampling is rarely used because few, if any, large target populations exist as lists of identifiable units. For these reasons, most researchers in the behavioral sciences gather information from a **convenience sample** of individuals who are nearby and thus readily available.

Convenience Sampling

At some larger research universities, the list of available participants is composed of students who sign up for various studies as a requirement of the major. Students who elect not to be research participants must choose some alternative exercise that is deemed to be equivalent in terms of time and effort to complete as well as educational value. Convenience samples may also be composed of individuals who passively volunteer as members of intact groups (e.g., classes or meetings of some sort) who need only remain in the room to participate. Because convenience samples were not randomly selected from a population, the extent to which findings based on such samples may be generalized to the population—that is, the external validity of the results—is usually limited. However, the most important findings are almost always **replicated** by other researchers, using different convenience samples of individuals in places that may differ culturally as well as geographically from the location of the original study. A failure to replicate the basic findings of an original study usually means that those findings may not be generalized beyond the context in which they were obtained. On the other hand, successful replication of a finding using different convenience samples extends the generalizability of that finding.

A **volunteer**, or *self-selected*, **sample** is a special kind of convenience sample composed of individuals who choose to sign up for an experiment or to complete a mailed, telephone, or online survey without additional prompting. Findings based on volunteer samples are particularly suspect because the personality and demographic characteristics of volunteers tend to differ from those of individuals who do not actively volunteer. Indeed, the differences between a volunteer sample and a sample of randomly selected individuals are usually more exaggerated than the differences between a more typical convenience sample and a randomly selected sample. Note here that such volunteer samples should not be confused with students who "volunteer" to participate in a study to satisfy a course or major requirement or with randomly selected individuals who agree to participate by signing an informed consent agreement.

The Problem with a Biased Sample

This section of the chapter pits a single individual's testimony about the effectiveness of a cosmetic against statistical reasoning. How should an intelligent consumer evaluate a product that is endorsed in this fashion? Following the logic of statistical inference, one might consider the following questions:

- Is the sample, one 60-year-old woman, representative of the population of individuals who might benefit from using the product?
- How likely is a positive report if the product is really no better than any other product of its kind?

Regarding the first question, the report of a single individual, no matter how glowing, can never be a representative sample. The problem of sample bias is compounded in this instance by the fact that this is a volunteer (self-selected) sample of one individual who, at 60 years of age, is using a product targeted for a much younger group of consumers and is therefore unlikely to be representative of her age group. The second question can not be separated from the first: If the sample is a single biased testimonial, the likelihood of a positive response to a product that is no better than its competition is high. Any decision about the effectiveness of a product that is based on an unusual sample is likely to be flawed.

Random Assignment

As you learned in Chapter 1, the defining characteristic of an experiment is the random assignment of participants to groups or conditions. **Random assignment** ensures that each participant has an equal chance of being assigned to each experimental condition. So, random *assignment* shares with random *selection* the use of a random process, but the procedures are used for different reasons and should not be confused. Random assignment is the most effective means of accomplishing two objectives: (1) to eliminate experimenter bias in the assignment of participants to experimental conditions, and (2) to evenly distribute potentially confounding participant characteristics (education, gender, income, intelligence, personality, sensory acuity, etc.) across the different conditions of an experiment. Recall from Chapter 1 that a confounding variable is one whose effects are "mixed up" or "confounded" with those of the independent variable. If some random process is not used to assign participants to groups, the study will likely be confounded at the outset by preexisting group differences. After administering the independent variable manipulation, any differences between the dependent variable scores in the groups may be due to the effect of the independent variable, or to preexisting group differences, or to both. The results are thereby confounded, and any conclusions regarding the effect of the independent variable are rendered suspect by the ambiguity of the research design.

> Probability

A contestant on the "Who Wants to Be a Millionaire" television program phones a friend to get an answer to a question that has her stumped. When the friend offers an answer, the contestant asks her friend how certain she is that her answer is correct. A typical response is usually expressed as a percentage such as "I'm about 70 percent sure." This answer is an example of a **subjective probability** (also called **personal probability**), an intuitive feeling about the chance that a successful outcome will occur (such as providing a correct answer). In statistics, the probability of an outcome is determined objectively by observing the frequency with which an outcome occurs over a very large number of trials. You may wonder why it is necessary to observe the outcomes of a very large number of independent trials. A coin has two sides, so why isn't the probability that it will land on one side or the other equal to 0.5? Expressed more formally, why not just compute the probability of a success (e.g., a coin landing heads) as the number of ways that a success can occur over the total number of possible outcomes? The answer is that this method of determining probability assumes that the coin is perfectly balanced. There is simply no way to test that assumption apart from flipping the coin an infinitely large number of times. Because no one can flip a coin an infinite number of times[1], statisticians settle for the "long-run" (i.e., a repetition of many, many trials) interpretation of expected-frequency probability.

The familiar example of flipping a coin will be used to provide examples of the following definitions:

- A **trial** is a single coin flip.
- An **outcome** is the result of a trial; a coin can land either heads or tails.
- A **success** is an outcome of interest such as a coin landing heads.
- The *frequency* of a particular outcome, usually the one defined as a success, is the number of times the outcome was observed in a given set of independent trials.
- The *relative frequency* of a success is the number of times the outcome occurred relative to the number of times it could have occurred. If the frequency of heads is 47 out of 100 trials, then the relative frequency of heads is 47 / 100 = 0.47.
- *Proportion* is another name for relative frequency.
- *Percentage* is a proportion expressed as frequency per 100 trials. Multiplying any proportion by 100 converts the proportion to a percentage.
- *Expected relative frequency* is the relative frequency of successes that would be expected to occur in a very large number of independent trials—in "the long run" (law of large numbers).

---

[1] There have been some valiant efforts by some notable people in the history of statistics. For example, Karl Pearson flipped a coin 24,000 times and counted heads 12,012 times (50.05%). South African mathematician John Kerrich spent much of World War II in a prison camp in Jutland, courtesy of the Nazi regime. While there, he flipped a coin 10,000 times and counted 5,067 heads (50.67%).

- **Expected relative frequency probability** is the likelihood of observing a success expressed as an expected relative frequency.

When expressed as a *proportion*, a probability value ranges between 0 and 1. When expressed as a *percent chance*, a probability can be any value between 0 and 100. The following are equivalent statements:

- The probability of selecting 1 of 800 winning tickets for a lottery in which 1,000,000 tickets were sold is .0008.
- The proportion of winning lottery tickets is .0008.
- The percentage of winning lottery tickets is .08.
- There is a .08 percent chance of purchasing 1 of the winning lottery tickets.
- The odds are 9,992 to 8 against winning the lottery.

The expected relative frequency probability of an outcome of interest (a success) is determined as follows:

$$p(\text{success}) = \frac{\text{number of successes}}{\text{number of trials}}$$

Independence and Probability

Please do not miss the point that expected relative frequency probabilities are defined over a very large number of *independent* trials. An *independent* trial is one whose outcome is not influenced by the outcome of any previous trial. The coin does not "remember" whether it landed heads or tails on the previous trial or the ones before that, so each flip results in an outcome that is not affected in any way by the result of any previous trial.

> Inferential Statistics

Developing Hypotheses

Hypothesis testing begins with data collection which, in turn, involves an identification of a target population, sampling from that population, assigning participants to two or more groups or conditions, and selecting an independent variable and a dependent variable. In the example described in the text, a researcher compared calorie estimates made for two pictures. For the purpose of additional practice, let's work through another example. Imagine a researcher randomly selects a sample of 60 students from the sophomore class of a university then randomly assigns half the students to an experimental group and half to a control group. The students assigned to the **experimental group** will be exposed to the experimental treatment, a semester-long program administered through the university's career center that features weekly hour-long meetings during which they learn about various graduate school and career options. Students assigned to the **control group** also attend weekly hour-long meetings over the course of the semester, but they do not receive information about career and graduate school options. The independent variable in this study is the kind of program the students are assigned to attend, and its two levels are defined by the presence and absence of information about career and graduate school options. Because the students are randomly assigned to the two groups, the only difference between them is the level of the independent variable to which they are exposed. At the end of the semester, both groups complete the Consideration of Future Consequences (CFC) scale. Their scores on the CFC scale serve as the dependent variable.

The **null hypothesis** to be tested in this study is that attending the weekly career center program meetings will not affect CFC scores—that is, the mean CFC score in the population of students who are exposed to information about career and graduate school options is the same as that of the population of students who are not exposed to such information. The null hypothesis is described in the text as the "boring" hypothesis, because it is the hypothesis that says nothing is going on: no effect of the independent variable and thus no difference between the mean scores in the two populations of students. The university administrators hope that the evidence will permit a rejection of the null hypothesis in favor of the alternative called the research hypothesis. The **research hypothesis** in this example states that the mean CFC score in the population of students who are exposed to information about career and graduate school options is *not* the same as that of the population of students who are not exposed to such information. The research hypothesis could also be expressed as a directional statement: The mean CFC score in the population of students who are exposed to information about career and graduate school options is *greater than* that of the population of students who are not exposed to such information. If the research hypothesis is a directional statement, then the null hypothesis must be a directional statement as well: The mean CFC score in the population of students who are exposed to information about career and graduate school options is *less than or equal to* that of the population of students who are not exposed to such information. The research hypothesis is the "exciting hypothesis" in the sense that it declares that providing students information about their post-graduation plans will encourage them to get a head start researching and planning for their futures—actions that indicate a consideration of future consequences.

Making a Decision

Based on an analysis of our data, we make a decision to either *reject* or *fail to reject* the null hypothesis. Please note that failing to reject the null hypothesis is not the same as "accepting" it. It is never appropriate to "accept" or "conclude support for" the null hypothesis. If the null hypothesis is not rejected, then the results are *inconclusive* regarding the validity of the null hypothesis. Of course, the university administrators hope to be able to reject the null hypothesis because doing so will allow them to conclude support for the research hypothesis. This is the somewhat convoluted logic of hypothesis testing. A researcher is obligated to test a hypothesis that she does not believe to be true and hopes to be able to reject so she can conclude support for its logical opposite—the research hypothesis. This logic is not entirely strange, however. A prosecuting attorney goes through a similar procedure when he is obliged to assume that a defendant is innocent even while he attempts to persuade the jury with compelling logic and evidence that the defendant is guilty beyond a reasonable doubt.

In making a decision regarding the null hypothesis, it is possible that the decision is in error. The two types of errors are discussed in the next section, but for now you should note that it is impossible to avoid decision errors. The only way for researchers to know whether they are making a decision error is to know whether the null hypothesis is true. Of course, if this were known, then there would be no reason to test the null hypothesis. Thus, researchers can not know whether they are making a decision error when they reject or fail to reject the null hypothesis, so they can not avoid committing decision errors. For this reason, it is never appropriate to use any forms of the words "prove" or "true" when interpreting the results of a hypothesis test. The possibility of making an error when deciding whether to reject or to fail to reject the null hypothesis means that it is not possible to "prove" that the null hypothesis is "true" or "false." If the null hypothesis is rejected, the appropriate conclusion is that the results support the research hypothesis. If the null hypothesis is not rejected, then the researcher should conclude simply that the results do not support the research hypothesis.

> Type I and Type II Errors

As discussed above, each test of a null hypothesis requires a decision to either reject, or fail to reject, the hypothesis. As shown in the following table, two errors are possible. A **Type I error** occurs when a true null hypothesis is rejected, whereas a **Type II error** is committed when a researcher fails to reject a false null hypothesis.

Status of the Null Hypothesis

Researcher's Decision	The null hypothesis is true	The null hypothesis is false
Reject the null hypothesis	Type I Error	Correct Decision
Do not reject the null hypothesis	Correct Decision	Type II Error

Hypothesis testing in science has traditionally regarded a Type I error as more serious than a Type II error. As the authors of our text note, both errors can have considerable negative consequences.

STUDY QUESTIONS

1. Which one of the following statements about sampling is most accurate?
   a. The laws of probability require that a representative sample include at least 50% of the units in a population.
   b. A large sample is always more representative than a smaller sample, regardless of how the units are sampled.
   c. When a sample is used to represent a population, there is always a risk of reaching an inaccurate conclusion about the population.
   d. A sample of one individual may sometimes be representative of an entire population.

2. The goal of sampling is to obtain _____ sample.
   a. a representative
   b. a simple random
   c. the largest possible
   d. the smallest possible

3. A(n) _____ sample is one in which every member of the population has an equal chance of being selected to participate in a study.

4. If a school psychologist obtained a list of all 2000 students enrolled in a certain high school and randomly selected 50 students from the list, her sample would most accurately be termed a _____ sample.
   a. convenience
   b. simple random
   c. stratified random
   d. cluster

5. Which one of the following statements about random samples is *most* accurate?
   a. Random samples are composed of individuals who had the highest probability of being selected.
   b. Random samples are almost never used because researchers almost never have access to an entire population.
   c. The results of studies based on random samples of participants are generally very low in external validity.
   d. Random samples are common in the social and behavioral sciences, but are extremely rare in the natural sciences.

6. The goal that underlies every sampling technique is to:
   a. produce a diverse sample of individuals, regardless of the makeup of the population.
   b. give each individual in the population an equal chance of being selected.
   c. include simple random sampling at some stage in the process.
   d. produce a sample that is representative of the population.

7. Which of the following sequences of numbers would be considered the *least* random by people who do not understand randomness?
   a. 35963
   b. 61962
   c. 75246
   d. 33351

8. Which one of the following is *most* likely to be a random sequence?
   a. 01010101
   b. 11110000
   c. 11111111
   d. These sequences are equally likely.

9. The **generalizability** of research findings refers to the application of those findings:
   a. to solve problems in theoretical fields such as experimental psychology.
   b. from one sample or in one context to other samples or contexts.
   c. to solve problems in applied fields such as clinical psychology.
   d. from a population to a sample of individuals.

10. A _____ sample is composed of participants who were selected because of their ready availability.
    a. random
    b. quota
    c. probability
    d. convenience

11. Suppose that a student researcher distributes surveys to her friends, students who live on her hall, and fellow members of campus clubs. This student's method of selecting participants for her research project is most similar to the procedure used to select a _____ sample.
    a. cluster
    b. convenience
    c. simple random
    d. stratified random

12. A **volunteer sample**:
    a. is a kind of convenience sample.
    b. is a kind of stratified random sample.
    c. may be distinguished from a self-selected sample.
    d. is more similar to a random sample than to a convenience sample.

13. According to the text, the "activity [that] reduces the risks of a convenience sample more than any other" is _____.
    a. replication
    b. random sampling
    c. random assignment
    d. using a randomized block design

14. The **replication** of a scientific study:
    a. is a form of plagiarism.
    b. should ideally be as identical as possible to the original study.
    c. can compensate to some degree for an inability to sample randomly from a population.
    d. is not possible unless participants are randomly selected from the population of interest.

15. Who among the following students would be *least* likely to bias the results of a study in which he or she volunteered to participate?
    a. Susan, who responded to an advertisement in a student newspaper to earn some extra money
    b. Dan, who signed an informed consent agreement after being randomly selected from a list of eligible students
    c. Mary, who thought that participating in a faculty member's research project as a course requirement would be easier than the alternative—writing a 10-page research paper
    d. Phil, who needed the extra credit points to earn a passing grade in his statistics class

16. Which one of the following statements is *most* accurate?
    a. Random assignment requires a sample of research participants who were randomly selected from the population of interest.
    b. Random assignment almost always results in a sample that is adequately representative of the population of interest.
    c. Research findings are generally replicated only if both random selection and random assignment are used.
    d. Random selection is almost never used, whereas random assignment is frequently used in behavioral science research.

17. Random assignment:
    a. is used to select a representative sample from a population.
    b. is used only when it is not feasible to randomly select participants from the population.
    c. guarantees that each participant has an equal chance of being assigned to one of the conditions of an experiment.
    d. guarantees that each individual within a population has an equal chance of being selected to participate in an experiment.

18. Which one of the following is an example of **subjective probability**?
    a. The probability of drawing a face card from a standard deck of playing cards is 12 / 52.
    b. There is a 70% chance of rain today, because it has rained on 70% of days like this in the past.
    c. Of the winners of the 41 Super Bowls, 8 teams won in consecutive years; therefore, the chance that the Indianapolis Colts will repeat as Super Bowl champions is 8 out of 41.
    d. Peyton Manning is 90% confident that the Indianapolis Colts will repeat as Super Bowl champions.

19. Aunt Sophie thinks that there is a 100% chance that it will rain because she "feels it in her bones." Aunt Sophie's belief is an example of:
    a. the gambler's fallacy.
    b. an expected relative frequency probability.
    c. a subjective probability.
    d. a confirmation bias.

20. Rex is flipping a coin to see how often it lands heads. In the language of probability, each flip of the coin is called a(n) _____.
    a. success
    b. trial
    c. outcome
    d. event

21. Rex is flipping a coin to see how often it lands heads. In the language of probability, each time the coin lands either heads or tails is called a(n) _____.
    a. success
    b. trial
    c. outcome
    d. event

22. Which of the following is an example of an **expected relative-frequency probability**?
    a. There are 52 cards in a standard deck, so the chance of drawing an ace of spades is 1 in 52.
    b. Mary estimates that there is a 75% chance that her best friend will have a baby girl because Mary has guessed correctly on three out of the last four pregnancies.
    c. Joe expects that 10 flips of a fair coin will result in 5 heads and 5 tails.
    d. If you keep flipping a coin, the proportion of heads will eventually be very close to 0.5.

23. In statistics, **probability** is defined as the:
    a. number of times a particular outcome has occurred in the past.
    b. number of times a particular outcome will occur in the future.
    c. level of confidence that a particular outcome will occur.
    d. expected relative frequency of a particular outcome.

Use the following passage to answer questions 24–27.

One hundred students were randomly selected from the sophomore class of a mid-sized university to participate in a study designed to increase student interest in pursuing internships and research opportunities before their junior year. Fifty of the students were randomly assigned to attend weekly hour-long meetings during which counselors from the university's career center would discuss with them career opportunities for employment and graduate school options. The remaining 50 students also attended weekly hour-long meetings during which various campus issues were discussed, but there were no discussions of graduate school or career options. At the end of the fall semester, the Consideration of Future Consequences (CFC) scale was administered to the students in both groups.

24. The students assigned to attend weekly meetings during which they discussed career opportunities and graduate schools options with career center counselors comprised the:
    a. control group.
    b. experimental group.
    c. population of interest.
    d. research hypothesis group.

25. Which one of the following is an appropriate null hypothesis for this study?
    a. The CFC scores of the students assigned to the experimental group are not the same as those of the students assigned to the control group.
    b. The CFC scores of the students assigned to the experimental group are the same as those of the students assigned to the control group.
    c. The CFC scores of the students assigned to the experimental group are higher than those of the students assigned to the control group.
    d. The CFC scores in the populations represented by students in the experimental and control groups are the same.

26. Suppose that the mean CFC scores for the experimental and control groups are almost identical. The researcher should decide to:
    a. reject the research hypothesis.
    b. accept the null hypothesis.
    c. reject the null hypothesis.
    d. fail to reject the null hypothesis.

27. Suppose that the mean CFC score for the experimental group is much higher than the mean CFC score for the control group. In fact, the difference between the two group means is so large that it would occur by chance in fewer than 5 in 10,000 studies like the one described. Which one of the following is an appropriate conclusion?
    a. This result proves that the null hypothesis is false.
    b. This result proves that the research hypothesis is true.
    c. The results of this study were probably due to chance factors.
    d. The null hypothesis is almost certainly false and should be rejected.

28. Which of the following is a (are) correct statement(s) regarding the **null hypothesis**?
    a. The null hypothesis is sometimes called the alternative hypothesis.
    b. The null hypothesis is the one that a researcher cares the most about.
    c. The null hypothesis claims the opposite of what the researcher predicts.
    d. The null hypothesis is usually more accurate than the research hypothesis.

29. Which of the following is the most accurate description of a **research hypothesis**?
    a. It usually indicates a situation in which there is no difference between two populations.
    b. It is usually a more specific statement that the statement of the null hypothesis.
    c. It is also called the alternative (to the null) hypothesis.
    d. It is usually not as exciting as the null hypothesis.

30. A **Type I error** occurs when the:
    a. null hypothesis is incorrectly rejected.
    b. research hypothesis is incorrectly rejected.
    c. experimental group mean is not higher than the control group mean.
    d. data do not support either the research hypothesis or the null hypothesis.

31. A researcher who rejects a false null hypothesis has made a _____.
    a. Type I error
    b. Type II error
    c. correct decision
    d. Type I error as well as a Type II error

32. Suppose that a parole board has to decide whether a prisoner, a convicted murderer, is to be released. The null hypothesis states that the prisoner has not been rehabilitated. Which one of the following decisions represents a Type I error?
    a. The prisoner is released and kills a family of five in cold blood within 48 hours.
    b. The prisoner is released and becomes a model citizen.
    c. The prisoner is denied release when in fact he has been totally rehabilitated.
    d. The prisoner is denied release when in fact he remains an extremely dangerous man.

33. Suppose that a parole board has to decide whether a prisoner, a convicted murderer, is to be released. The null hypothesis states that the prisoner has not been rehabilitated. Which one of the following decisions represents a correct acceptance of the null hypothesis?
    a. The prisoner is released and becomes a model citizen.
    b. The prisoner is denied release when in fact he has been totally rehabilitated.
    c. The prisoner is denied release when in fact he remains an extremely dangerous man.
    d. The logic of hypothesis testing does not permit acceptance of the null hypothesis.

ANSWERS TO CHAPTER 5 STUDY QUESTIONS

Question Number	Correct Answer
1	c, pp. 94–97
2	a, p. 95
3	random (pp. 95–96)
4	b, pp. 95–96
5	b, pp. 95–96
6	d, p. 96
7	d, p. 96
8	d, p. 96
9	b, p. 96
10	d, pp. 96–97
11	b, pp. 96–97
12	a, p. 97
13	a, p. 97
14	c, p. 97
15	b, pp. 97–98
16	d, p. 98
17	c, pp. 98–99
18	d, p. 100

Question Number	Correct Answer
19	c, p. 100
20	b, p. 100
21	c, p. 100
22	d, p. 100
23	d, p. 100–101
24	b, p. 103
25	d, p. 104 (Hypothesis statements are always about populations.)
26	d, pp. 104–105
27	d, pp. 104–105
28	c, p. 104
29	c, p. 104
30	a, p. 107
31	c, pp. 107–108
32	a, p. 107
33	d, pp. 107–108 (The logic of hypothesis testing requires that the null hypothesis either be rejected or not rejected; it does not permit the acceptance of the null hypothesis.)

CHAPTER 6

The Normal Curve, Standarization, and *z* Scores

CHAPTER OUTLINE

The Normal Curve

Standardization, z Scores, and the Normal Curve
- The Need for Standardization
- Transforming Raw Scores into z Scores
- Transforming z Scores into Raw Scores
- Using z Scores to Make Comparisons
- Transforming z Scores into Percentiles

The Central Limit Theorem
- Creating a Distribution of Means
- Characteristics of the Distribution of Means
- Using the Central Limit Theorem to Make Comparisons with z Scores

LEARNING OBJECTIVES

After studying this chapter, you should be able to:

1. Define each of the following terms and provide examples that are not in the text: *normal curve, standardization, z score, z distribution, standard normal distribution, central limit theorem, distribution of means, standard error,* and *z statistic.*

2. Identify the individual who derived the formula for the normal curve and discuss the importance of this discovery to inferential statistics.

3. Explain how the process of *standardization* may be used "to compare apples to oranges"; that is, you should be able to explain how individual scores from different normal distributions may be converted to standard (*z*) scores and directly compared as percentiles of the *standard normal distribution.*

4. Paraphrase the *central limit theorem* and identify the two important principles demonstrated by the theorem. In particular, you should be able to explain the principle that specifies a normal *distribution of means* of samples that were randomly selected from a population of individ-

ual scores that are not distributed in the form of a normal curve. In addition, you should be able to explain why a distribution of sample means is less variable than a distribution of individual scores.

5. Distinguish between the standard deviation of a population of individual scores (σ) and the standard deviation of the population of all possible means of samples of a fixed size that are randomly selected from that population (called the *standard error* and symbolized with a subscript: σ_M).

6. Demonstrate how the mean of a sample of N scores may be compared to all other means of samples of N scores by converting the mean to a *z* statistic.

CHAPTER REVIEW

> The Normal Curve

The normal curve is probably the most familiar figure in statistics. The curve's widespread use in the behavioral and social sciences is based on studies showing that the shapes of the frequency distributions of a number of variables are well approximated by the normal curve. However, it is important to remember that the curve itself was derived mathematically, apparently before anyone noticed that a large number of variables seemed to have a bell-shaped distribution. The French expatriate Abraham De Moivre (1667-1754) is credited with deriving the formula used to draw the normal curve, although a sketch of the curve does not appear in any of his published work. The normal curve depicted on the next page was created in SPSS and is presented here to illustrate the curve's properties as discussed in the text.

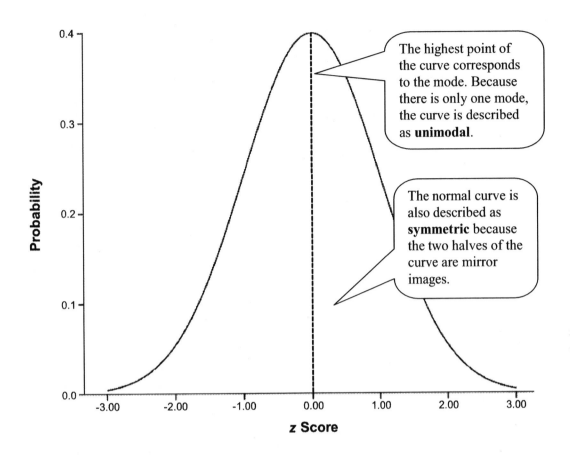

Think of a variable (a characteristic that varies) and the chances are good that the distribution of that variable has a shape that is very similar to the normal curve. The normal curve seems to be *ubiquitous* or everywhere at once. Practically speaking, the ubiquity of the normal curve means that the curve and its associated percentiles may be applied to the frequency distributions (histograms or polygons) of a very large number of variables that are of interest to scientists in a variety of disciplines.

In De Moivre's case, the practical application of the normal curve was in providing a foundation for determining the probability of various outcomes in games of chance. De Moivre earned a meager living as a math tutor and as a consultant to gamblers ("adventurers" or "gamesters" as he called them) who frequented Slaughter's Coffee House in London. It was in this latter role that he developed the equation for the normal curve as the limit of a probability distribution of chance outcomes. To get an idea of De Moivre's problem, consider the possible patterns of outcomes when a coin is flipped N times. When $N = 1$, there are just two outcomes, a head (H) or a tail (T). When $N = 2$, there are four possible outcomes (HH, HT, TH, and TT), and when $N = 3$, there are eight outcomes (HHH, HHT, HTH, THH, TTH, THT, HTT, and TTT). As you can see, for each addition of one trial, the number of outcomes doubles, so when *N* is just 20, the number of outcomes exceeds one million! Performing these calculations by hand was all but impossible, so de Moivre needed some means of determining the probability of a given outcome for any number of trials. De Moivre's genius was to use pure mathematics to derive the equation of the normal curve as a means of specifying a probability distribution for any number of trials of a chance process. The following figure shows how well De Moivre's normal approximation works in assigning probabilities to outcomes in a game of coin toss.

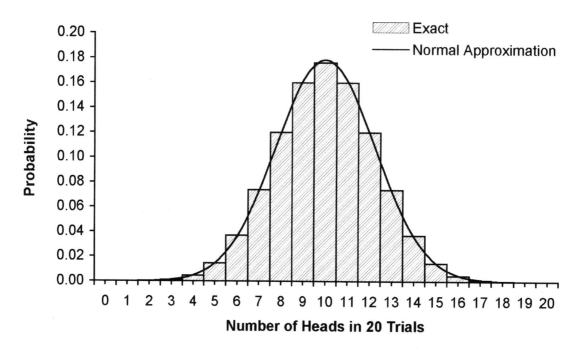

The histogram in the figure is the theoretical probability distribution of the frequency of heads in 20 trials if the coin is perfectly balanced and other ideal conditions are met. Notice how closely the shape of the probability histogram conforms to the normal curve. De Moivre showed that for an infinitely large number of trials, the probability of observing any number of heads is specified precisely by the normal curve. More practically, the probability distribution becomes progressively similar to the normal curve as the number of trials increases. We saw this in the text when our sample of heights increased from 5 students to 30 and then to 140 students. We can see it here again when the number of trials increases from 20 to 160.

When $N = 160$, the probability histogram is very closely approximated by a normal curve:

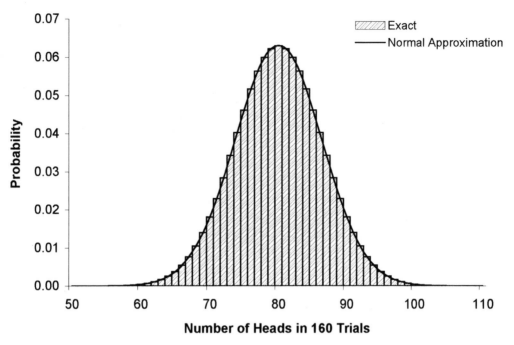

> ## Standardization, z Scores, and the Normal Curve

The Need for Standardization

Converting raw scores from different distributions into standard scores that share a common distribution permits us to make meaningful comparisons between the two originally dissimilar scores. Standard scores have a common mean, standard deviation, and we know how the data are distributed in terms of percentiles.

We convert raw scores into z scores, a specific kind of standard score, by assessing how many standard deviations a score is from its mean. We can do this for different scores measured on different scales. By converting scores to z scores, we assess how different the score is from average based on its own unique distribution, and we place the score on a common scale of measurement, the z distribution. This allows us to compare things that appear difficult to compare, such as the time it takes you to read this paragraph compared to how long it takes a 7-year-old to read something of equivalent length written at an appropriate reading level (assuming we know reading rates for these two populations, college students and 7-year-olds).

Transforming Raw Scores into z Scores

The process of **standardization** transforms a raw score to a score on a scale that has a mean of 0 and a standard deviation of 1. A raw score that has been standardized in this way is called a *standard score* or, more commonly, a z score. As long as the mean (μ) and the standard deviation (σ) of the population are known, any raw score X may be transformed to a z score. The following formula, is used to standardize a raw score:

$$z = \frac{X - \mu}{\sigma}$$

Expressed as a z score, the mean of any distribution of raw scores has a value of 0. Because the standard deviation of the z score scale is 1, any raw score that is 1 standard deviation above the mean has a value of 1, whereas a raw score that is 1 standard deviation below the mean has a value of –1. Suppose, for example, that the mean height in the population of female college students in the United States is 64.2 inches with a standard deviation of 2.57 inches. A student whose height is 66.77 inches is 1 standard deviation above the mean, so her height transformed to a score on the z scale is 1.

$$z = \frac{X - \mu}{\sigma} = \frac{66.77 - 64.2}{2.57} = 1$$

Similarly, a student who is 61.63 inches tall is 1 standard deviation below the mean, so her score on the z scale is –1.

$$z = \frac{X - \mu}{\sigma} = \frac{61.63 - 64.2}{2.57} = 1$$

Standardization enables meaningful comparisons between measures of different variables or between measures of the same variable between individuals from different populations. For example, a female college student who is 5 feet 8 inches tall may be meaningfully compared to a male college student who is 6 feet tall only after standardizing the height of each student. Assume the mean height for men is 69.6 inches with a standard deviation of 2.69 inches. Using the means and standard deviations provided, this works out to:

$$z_{Female} = \frac{68 - 64.2}{2.57} = 1.48 \qquad z_{Male} = \frac{72 - 69.6}{2.69} = 0.89$$

Relative to the appropriate comparison groups, the female student is taller than the male student by almost a half standard deviation.

Transforming z Scores into Raw Scores

Once a score has been translated into a z score, the formula can be reversed and the z score converted back into a raw score or a score expressed in its original units of measurement. Using the information provided about college students' heights and the formula from text page 127, we can convert the following z scores back into measurements of height in inches:

A woman with a z score for height of 2.0
$$X = z(\sigma) + \mu = 2.0\,(2.57) + 64.2 = 69.34 \text{ inches}$$

A man with a z score for height of –1.0
$$X = z(\sigma) + \mu = -1.0\,(2.69) + 69.6 = 66.91 \text{ inches}$$

Be sure to always check that your final answer makes sense. If the z score was negative, you should get a final answer below the mean; if the z score was positive, you should get a final answer above the mean.

By converting scores on different distributions into scores on a shared distribution, anything can be compared. The z scores we calculate are part of a z distribution that is normally distributed, with the mean, median, and mode all at the center of the distribution. Below the center are 50% of all scores, and above the center are the remaining 50% of the scores. This distribution is known as the standard normal distribution, and exact information about percentages for each z score has been computed. In other words, any score from a normally distributed population can be taken and converted to a z score and then assessed for what percentage of scores falls above or below it.

Using z Scores to Make Comparisons

In the text, we compared quiz scores in statistics classes with different means and standard deviations. Above, we compared the heights of men and women. Comparing the reading rates of a college student and a 7-year-old was also mentioned. Clearly, z scores are very useful in permitting us to make meaningful comparisons between scores from different distributions. Next, we learn how to add the valuable information about percentiles as we compare scores by converting them to z scores.

Transforming z Scores into Percentiles

Measures that are approximately normally distributed may also be compared by expressing their standard score equivalents as percentiles. As noted in the text, statisticians have calculated the percentages that fall under all areas of the normal curve. A few of these percentages are displayed in the figure on the following page:

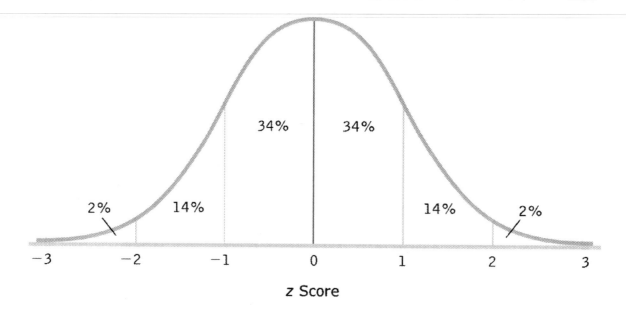

z Score

First, note that 50% (34% + 14% + 2% = 50%) of the scores are on either side of the mean of 0. Using the rounded percentages displayed in the figure, you can determine that a *z* score of 2 has 98% of score below it, because this score is greater than or equal to 50% + 34% + 14% = 98% of the scores in the population. Similarly, a *z* score of –1 has 2% + 14% = 16% of the scores in the population below it. The figure also shows that 34% + 34% = 68% of the scores are within 1 standard deviation of the mean, and 14% + 34% + 34% + 14% = 96% of the scores are within 2 standard deviations of the mean. As you can see, after we convert a score to a *z* score, we can say a lot more about the original raw score, including what percent of scores fall above and below it.

> The Central Limit Theorem

The central limit theorem is so-named because of its central importance in mathematical statistics. However, the theorem is also very important in behavioral research. This single theorem explains why so many variables have a normal distribution, but it also specifies the conditions that guarantee a normal distribution of sample means when the population of individual scores is not normally distributed.

The term **distribution of means** refers to the population of means computed for all possible samples of a given size (e.g., *N* = 20 or *N* = 50) from a population. (Statisticians commonly refer to the distribution of means as the *sampling distribution of the mean*.) You can think of building a distribution of means by sampling randomly and repeatedly, with replacement, from a population until every possible combination of *N* participants is sampled. Each time you select a sample of participants, you obtain a measure of some characteristic for each participant (e.g., height, measured in inches), compute the mean of the measures, and continue in this manner until you have computed the means of an infinitely large number of samples.

Obviously, you cannot sample an infinitely large number of times from a population, but this little thought experiment should give you a better understanding of what is meant by a distribution of means and perhaps make the following paraphrase of the **central limit theorem** a little easier to understand as well:

> Regardless of the shape of the distribution of individual scores in the population, the shape of the distribution of means from this population (the sampling distribution of the mean) will approach the shape of a normal curve as the size of the sample (*N*) grows large. In addition, the mean of the distribution of means is equal to the mean of the population, and the standard deviation of the distribution of means is equal to the standard deviation of the population divided by the square root of the sample size.

Creating a Distribution of Means

As an illustration of how the central limit theorem works, consider the possible sums that result when a pair of dice are tossed. As shown in the figure below (left), there are only $6^2 = 36$ possible sums, so this example will allow us to avoid thinking about an infinitely large number of samples. The figure on the right is a probability histogram of the 36 possible sums.

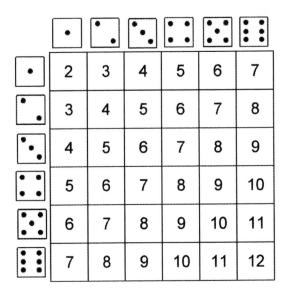
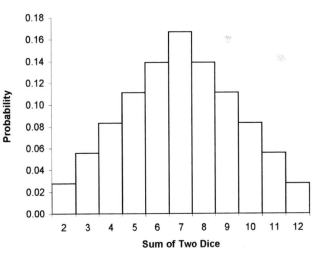

Each roll of the dice is analogous to randomly sampling 2 of the 6 die faces that comprise the entire population, and the probability histogram is the distribution of all possible sums of samples of $N = 2$ from this population. (We're using sums here instead of means but the distribution of sums has the same shape as a distribution of means. You may think of each sample sum as a sample mean multiplied by 2, the sample size.) The shape of the probability histogram is unimodal and symmetric, but it is not quite normal. According to the central limit theorem, we'll have to increase the sample size to get the shape of the probability histogram to look more like a normal curve.

Now notice what happens when the sample size is increased to 6. (With 6 dice, there are $6^6 = 46{,}656$ possible outcomes, so it is impractical to list them all.) In accord with the central limit theorem, the increase in the sample size from 2 to 6 results in a distribution of sums that is shaped more like a normal curve.

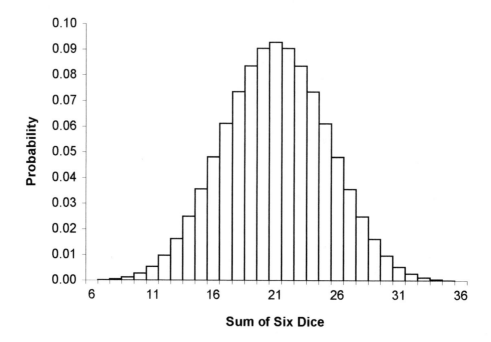

Please do not miss the point that the central limit theorem specifies the shape of the distribution of means (or sums) of *all possible samples* of a particular size. The central limit theorem is demonstrated by increasing the sample size (the number of dice in each roll), not the number of samples (rolls).

Characteristics of the Distribution of Means

Recall from the paraphrase of the central limit theorem above that it also specifies the mean and the standard deviation of the distribution of means. According to the central limit theorem, the mean of a distribution of sample means (the symbol is σ_M) is equal to the mean of the population (μ) from which the samples were selected. In symbols,

$$\mu = \mu_M$$

In the example of rolling 6 dice, the population mean may be computed by summing the 6 die faces and dividing by 6: $\mu = (6 + 5 + 4 + 3 + 2 + 1) / 6 = 21$

/ 6 = 3.5. Converting the distribution of 46,656 sample sums to a distribution of sample means is accomplished by dividing each sum by the sample size (6). The mean of the distribution of means is then computed by dividing the sum of the means by the number of means: $\mu_M = 163,296 / 46,656 = 3.5$. Note that these two means are the same.

The central limit theorem also relates the standard deviation of the distribution of means (σ_M) to the standard deviation of the parent population (σ):

$$\sigma_M = \frac{\sigma}{\sqrt{N}}$$

To avoid potential confusion, the standard deviation of the distribution of means is called the *standard error of the mean*, usually shortened to **standard error**. As you can see from the formula, the standard error is much smaller than the standard deviation of the population because means are less variable than individual scores. According to the formula, the size of the sample, N, is the key factor determining how much smaller the standard error will be relative to the standard deviation of the population.

As illustrated in the text, standard error becomes smaller as sample size increases. What this means is that as each mean is based on more and more data (larger sample size), the means better approximate the mean of the population. The result is that the distribution of sample means becomes narrower and narrower as sample size increases. In fact, if we sample to infinity, only one sample mean will be calculated and the distribution will be very narrow—with only one score.

Another point made here is that the distribution of means approximates a normal distribution even when the population from which the means are calculated is not normally distributed. If the population distribution is approximately normal, then the distribution of means will be approximately normal, regardless of the number of scores in the sample. However, if the population distribution is not normal, then the central limit theorem states that the distribution of means will be approximately normal if the sample size is sufficiently large ($N \geq 30$ or so).

In the next section, we will use the mean and standard error of the distribution of means to convert sample means to z statistics.

Using the Central Limit Theorem to Make Comparisons with z Scores

The central limit theorem may be applied to virtually any variable, including scores from rating scales, achievement tests, personality inventories, and intelligence tests, as well as measures such as height, weight, response rate, and reaction time. In short, the central limit theorem may be applied to any variable of interest to behavioral scientists. The practical importance of the central limit theorem, as mentioned above, is that it enables researchers to compare the mean of a sample of scores to the standard normal distribution, even though the scores themselves are not distributed normally in the population. If the scores *are* normally distributed, then the sample size doesn't matter. But if we aren't sure about the shape of the population, then we'll need a sample size of at least 30 or so to enlist the aid of the central limit theorem. In either case, using the standard normal distribution requires that we standardize the sample mean. We do this by converting the mean (M) to a z statistic using the following formula:

$$z = \frac{M - \mu_M}{\sigma_M}$$

The formula is similar to the formula used to compute a z score, so make sure that you do not confuse them. The most common error is to divide by the standard deviation (σ) instead of the standard error (σ_M). As noted in the previous section, the standard error is computed by dividing the standard deviation of the population by the square root of the sample size:

$$\sigma_M = \frac{\sigma}{\sqrt{N}}$$

STUDY QUESTIONS

1. Who among the following is credited with deriving the mathematical formula used to draw the normal curve?
   a. Abraham De Moivre
   b. Sir Isaac Newton
   c. Karl Pearson
   d. Karl Friedrich Gauss

2. The normal curve is *unimodal* which means that:
   a. there are as many scores above the mean as there are below the mean.
   b. most of the scores are in the middle with very few at the extremes.
   c. the areas to the left and right of the center are mirror images.
   d. probabilities may be computed from *z* scores.

3. The normal curve is *symmetric* which means that:
   a. there are as many scores above the mean as there are below the mean.
   b. most of the scores are in the middle with very few at the extremes.
   c. the areas to the left and right of the center are mirror images.
   d. probabilities may be computed from *z* scores.

4. The process of **standardization** converts raw scores to:
   a. percentiles.
   b. *z* scores.
   c. means.
   d. standard deviations.

5. The **standard normal distribution** is a distribution of:
   a. *z* scores.
   b. raw scores with a mean of 0 and a standard deviation of 1.
   c. raw scores with a mean of 50 and a standard deviation of 10.
   d. raw scores with a mean of 100 and a standard deviation of 15.

6. If scores on the Stanford-Binet IQ test are normally distributed with mean = 100 and standard deviation = 16, what is the percentage of scores between 100 and 116?
   a. 14
   b. 16
   c. 34
   d. 68

7. If scores on the Stanford-Binet IQ test are normally distributed with mean = 100 and standard deviation = 16, which one of the following intervals contains the fewest scores?
   a. 100–116
   b. 116–132
   c. 68–84
   d. 132–148

8. About _____ percent of Stanford-Binet IQ test scores (mean = 100, standard deviation = 16) are between 116 and 132.
   a. 16
   b. 84
   c. 68
   d. 14

9. If scores on the Stanford-Binet IQ test are normally distributed with mean = 100 and standard deviation = 16, what is the minimum score in the top 2%?
   a. 116
   b. 132
   c. 84
   d. 68

10. If a variable is normally distributed then approximately _____ percent of the values of that variable are within one standard deviation of the mean.
    a. 14
    b. 34
    c. 50
    d. 68

11. A certain student was disappointed with her performance on a recent statistics exam because she answered only 75 percent of the questions correctly. She later learned that the scores on the exam were normally distributed, and the instructor awarded grades based on standard (*z*) scores rather than percent correct. If this student's standard (*z*) score is exactly 2, then she should be:
    a. pleased that her score was in the top 2% of the class.
    b. disappointed that her standard score is so small.
    c. relieved that her score was in the average range.
    d. disappointed that her score had a percentile rank of 2.

12. If the heights of female college students are normally distributed, with mean = 65 inches and standard deviation = 2.5 inches, what percentage of these students are taller than 65 inches?
    a. 35%
    b. 50%
    c. 65%
    d. 68%

13. For any normally distributed variable, what is the percentage of scores between 1 standard deviation below, and 2 standard deviations above, the mean?
    a. 68
    b. 34
    c. 82
    d. 48

14. If grades on a certain test are approximately normally distributed with a mean of 75 and a standard deviation of 10, what percentage of the students received grades less than 65?
    a. 8%
    b. 16%
    c. 60%
    d. 84%

15. If grades on a certain test are approximately normally distributed with a mean of 75 and a standard deviation of 10, what percentage of the students received grades either less than 55 or greater than 95?
    a. 4%
    b. 9%
    c. 68%
    d. 96%

16. If grades on a certain test are approximately normally distributed with a mean of 75 and a standard deviation of 10, what is the lowest grade in the top 2% of grades on the test?
    a. 50
    b. 80
    c. 90
    d. 95

17. If grades on a certain test are approximately normally distributed with a mean of 75 and a standard deviation of 10, what is the highest grade in the bottom 2% of grades on the test?
    a. 55
    b. 65
    c. 85
    d. 95

18. If grades on a certain test are approximately normally distributed with a mean of 75 and a standard deviation of 10, what is the lowest grade in the top 50% of grades on the test?
    a. 90
    b. 85
    c. 75
    d. 50

19. The Web site for the ACT College Entrance Exam reports that the mean composite score of the graduating class of 2007 is 21.2. In addition, the site provides the percentiles for the full range of scores, from 1 to 36. Interpolating, the score at the 84th percentile rounds to 26, whereas the score at the 16th percentile is roughly 16. What is the approximate standard deviation of the ACT scores?
    a. 68
    b. 34
    c. 10
    d. 5

20. Suppose that you are a statistician's research assistant and your task is to use a computer to simulate the random selection, with replacement, of a very large number of samples from a population in which there are just five values, 1, 2, 3, 4, and 5, each of which has the same probability of being selected. According to the **central limit theorem**:
    a. the shape of the distribution of sample means will be approximately normal as long as the sample size is sufficiently large.
    b. as the number of samples increases, the shape of the distribution of sample means becomes more like the shape of a normal curve.
    c. as the number of samples increases, the shape of the distribution of sample means becomes more like the shape of the population.
    d. the shape of the distribution of sample means will be the same as the shape of the population, regardless of the size of each sample.

21. A researcher has just computed the mean of a sample of 50 scores. The probability of obtaining a sample mean as extreme as the one that she computed is found by comparing her sample mean to a comparison distribution of _____ from the population.
    a. 50 scores selected at random
    b. 50 means selected at random
    c. means of all samples of 50 scores
    d. means of 50 samples selected at random

22. A distribution of means is less variable than a distribution of individual scores because:
    a. means are insensitive to extreme scores.
    b. means pull extreme scores toward the center.
    c. outliers must be eliminated before computing the mean.
    d. samples almost never include extremely low or high scores.

23. Which of the following is correct regarding the distribution of means?
    a. The mean is the same as the mean of the population of individual scores from which the samples were taken.
    b. The standard error is the same as the standard deviation of the population of individual scores from which the samples were taken.
    c. The shape is approximately normal regardless of the shape of the population of individual scores and regardless of the sample size.
    d. The shape is normal only if the shape of the population of individual scores is normal.

24. Which of the following is (are) not needed to determine the mean, standard deviation, and shape of a distribution of means?
    a. the standard deviation of the population of individual scores
    b. the mean of the population of individual scores
    c. the number of scores in each sample
    d. samples from the population

25. You may compute the standard deviation of a distribution of means by:
    a. dividing the population standard deviation by the square root of the sample size.
    b. dividing the square of the population standard deviation by the sample size.
    c. dividing the square root of the population standard deviation and by the square root of the sample size.
    d. dividing the square of the population standard deviation by the square root of the sample size.

26. The **standard error** tells you how much _____ deviates from the mean of _____.
    a. each score in a sample; the population
    b. each score in a sample; the sample
    c. each sample mean; the distribution of means
    d. each score in the population; the population

27. In a certain population of college-bound high school seniors, the mean ACT score is 22 and the standard deviation is 4. The standard error of the distribution of means of samples of $N = 25$ from this population is _____.
    a. 64
    b. 16
    c. 4
    d. 0.8

28. Which one of the following is the correct formula for converting a sample mean to a z statistic?

    a. $\dfrac{X - \mu_M}{\dfrac{\sigma}{\sqrt{N}}}$
    b. $\dfrac{X - \mu_M}{\sigma}$
    c. $\dfrac{M - \mu_M}{\sigma}$
    d. $\dfrac{M - \mu_M}{\dfrac{\sigma}{\sqrt{N}}}$

29. A pizza delivery chain claims that it delivers its pizzas to any location within a 15 mile radius within an average of 30 minutes, with a standard deviation of 12 minutes. Suppose that a researcher employed by a competitor orders 16 pizzas to be delivered to different locations within a 15 mile radius, and computes a sample mean delivery time of 38 minutes. What is this mean delivery time expressed as a z statistic?
    a. 0.67
    b. −0.67
    c. 2.67
    d. −2.67

30. According to the Web site for the ACT College Entrance Exam, 1,300,599 high school seniors took the ACT test in 2007, earning a mean composite score of 21.1, with a standard deviation of 5.0. Suppose that the ACT is administered to a random sample of 100 students from the entire population of high school seniors and the sample mean is computed to be 22. How many standard errors separate this sample mean from the national mean?
    a. 0.16
    b. 0.5
    c. 1.6
    d. 4.02

ANSWERS TO CHAPTER 6 STUDY QUESTIONS

Question Number	Correct Answer	Question Number	Correct Answer
1	a, p. 118	17	a, p. 130 (see Figure 6.8)
2	b, p. 118	18	c, p. 130 (see Figure 6.8)
3	c, p. 118	19	d, p. 130 (see Figure 6.8)
4	b, p. 122	20	a, p. 132 [This is a paraphrase of the central limit theorem.]
5	a, p. 128		
6	c, p. 130 (see Figure 6.8)	21	c, p. 135
7	d, p. 130 (see Figure 6.8)	22	b, pp. 133–134
8	d, p. 130 (see Figure 6.8)	23	a, p. 135
9	b, p. 130 (see Figure 6.8)	24	d, pp. 134–136
10	d, pp. 130–131 (see Figure 6.8)	25	a, p. 136
11	a, pp. 130–131 (see Figure 6.8)	26	c, p. 135
12	b, p. 130 (see Figure 6.8)	27	d, p. 136
13	c, p. 130 (see Figure 6.8)	28	d, p. 137
14	b, p. 130 (see Figure 6.8)	29	c, pp. 137–138
15	a, p. 130 (see Figure 6.8)	30	c, pp. 137–138
16	d, p. 130 (see Figure 6.8)		

Hypothesis Testing with z Tests

LEARNING OBJECTIVES

After studying this chapter, you should be able to:

1. Define each of the following terms and provide examples that are not in the text: *assumptions*; *robust*; *parametric tests*; *nonparametric tests*, *critical values*, *critical region*; *p levels (or alphas)*, *statistically significant*, *one-tailed test*, and *two-tailed test*.

2. Provide solutions to problems and exercises that involve converting raw scores to standard scores and using the standard normal probability distribution (the z distribution) to determine percentile ranks and assign probabilities to values of normally distributed variables.

3. Provide solutions to problems and exercises that involve converting sample means to z statistics and using the standard normal probability distribution to assign probabilities to intervals within a sampling distribution of normally distributed means.

4. Enumerate and explain the six steps of hypothesis testing.

5. Apply the six steps of hypothesis testing to conduct a z test of a null hypothesis about the value of a population mean when the population standard deviation is known.

CHAPTER REVIEW

> **The *z* Table**

In this chapter, the six steps of traditional hypothesis testing are formally introduced in the context of conducting a one-sample *z* test. As background, you may wish to review the definition of hypothesis testing in Chapter 1 (text page 10) as well as the general logic underlying all hypothesis testing procedures in Chapter 5 (text pages 103–106).

Raw Scores, z Scores and Percentages

To provide additional background for conducting the *z* test, this chapter begins with a continuation of the discussion of standardization that began in Chapter 6. Recall from that discussion that any raw score (*X*) may be standardized by converting it to a standard, or *z*, score. The practical utility of converting raw scores to *z* scores is to facilitate comparisons between measures of different variables—the "apples to oranges" comparisons that were described in Chapter 6. You also learned in Chapter 6 that the distributions of many variables of interest to behavioral scientists are well-approximated by a famous probability distribution called the normal curve. The *standardization* of a normally distributed variable places the values of that variable within the *standard* normal distribution, also known as the *z* distribution. After a normally distributed variable is standardized, its percentile rank may be determined from Table B.1 in the appendix of the text, which is covered in this section.

You also learned in Chapter 6 that standardization is not limited to raw scores but may be extended to the means of samples of raw scores as well. In addition, you learned that the means of samples selected from a population of normally distributed raw scores are themselves normally distributed. Finally, you learned that the central limit theorem ensures that the sampling distribution of the mean of sufficiently large samples (*N* > 30 or so) is normal even if the population of raw scores is not. Converting a sample mean to a *z* statistic enables the researcher to determine the probability of observing a sample mean as extreme as the one observed if the null hypothesis is true. This assignment of probability values to *z* (and other test) statistics is the foundation of statistical inference and of most of the hypothesis testing procedures available to researchers.

First, we will use the standard normal curve (*z* distribution) to determine the percentile rank of a normally distributed variable value such as an individual's score on an IQ test. Then, we will reverse this process and use information in the form of percentages to determine individual scores. For both types of problems, it will often be helpful to sketch the curve to help you visualize the solution. In the first type of problem, you are given a raw score (*X*), as well as the mean (*μ*) and the standard deviation (*σ*) of the population or comparison group, and you are asked to determine:

- the percentage of raw scores greater than *X*, or
- the percentage of raw scores less than *X* (this percentage is called the percentile rank), or
- the percentage of scores between two raw scores, X_1 and X_2.

The solution to each of these problems involves three (3) general steps.

If you are asked to determine the percentage of raw scores *greater than X*, follow these steps:

Step 1. Convert the raw score to a *z* score:

$$z = \frac{(X - \mu)}{\sigma}$$

Step 2. Use the table of normal curve percentages (Table B.1 in the appendix of the text, pp. B1–B3) to find the value of *z* that you computed in Step 1. An excerpt from the table follows:

z	% MEAN TO z	% IN TAIL
.00	0.00	50.00
.01	0.40	49.60
.02	0.80	49.20
.03	1.20	48.80
.04	1.60	48.40
.05	1.99	48.01

Step 3. If *z* is a positive value, then look in the column labeled "% IN TAIL" to find the percentage of raw scores greater than *X*. If *z* is a negative value, then look in the column labeled "% MEAN TO *z*" and add the value from this column to 50%.

If you are asked to determine the percentage of raw scores *less than X*, follow these steps:

Step 1. Convert the raw score to a *z* score:

$$z = \frac{(X - \mu)}{\sigma}$$

Step 2. Use the table of normal curve percentages to find the value of *z* that you computed in Step 1.

Step 3. Look in the % MEAN TO *z* column to find the percentage of raw scores between the mean and *z*. If *z* is above the mean (i.e., if *z* is a positive value), then the solution is found by adding 50% to the value in the % MEAN TO *z* column. If *z* is below the mean (i.e., if *z* is negative), then the solution is found by subtracting the value from the % MEAN TO *z* column from 50%.

If you are asked to determine the percentage of raw scores between two raw scores, say, X_1 *and* X_2, follow these steps:

Step 1. Convert each raw score to a z score:

$$z_1 = \frac{(X_1 - \mu)}{\sigma} \qquad z_2 = \frac{(X_2 - \mu)}{\sigma}$$

Step 2. Use the table of normal curve percentages to find the values of z_1 and z_2 that you computed in Step 1.

Step 3. Look in the % MEAN TO z column to find the percentage of raw scores between the mean and z_1 and between the mean and z_2. If z_1 and z_2 are on opposite sides of the mean, the solution is simply to sum the two percentages. If z_1 and z_2 are on the same side of the mean, subtract the smaller percentage from the larger one.

In the text, you also learned how to determine the percentage of scores that is at least as extreme as the score you are assessing.

Example Problem

Tom's IQ was measured to be 127. For Tom's comparison group, the mean IQ score is 100 and the standard deviation is 15. What is the percentile rank of Tom's IQ score—that is, what percentage of IQ scores in Tom's comparison group is less than Tom's score?

Solution

1. Tom's IQ score converts to a z score as follows:

$$Z_{IQ} = \frac{(127 - 100)}{15} = \frac{27}{15} = 1.8$$

2. Look up z = 1.8 in Table B.1 and find % MEAN TO z to be 46.41%. This is the percentage of scores between Tom's score and the mean score of 100. Now add 50% to 46.41% to get the answer: Tom's IQ score has a percentile rank of **96.41**—that is, his score is greater than 96.41% of the scores in his comparison group.

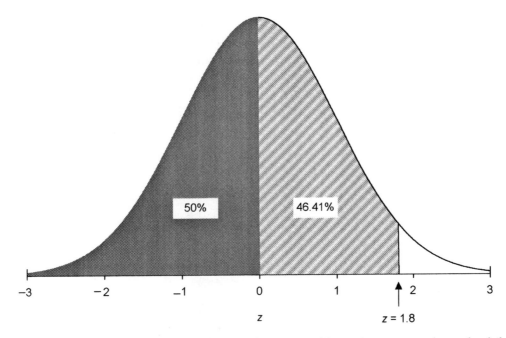

In the second type of normal curve problem, the mean and standard deviation of an appropriate comparison group of scores as well as a percentage of scores above or below a certain score are given. The problem requires that you find a *z* score that corresponds to this percentage, and may require that you convert the *z* score to a raw score. The solution to this type of problem involves just a few steps as well.

Step 1. Determine whether the percentage that you are given corresponds to a "% IN TAIL" or a "% MEAN TO *z*" and find the percentage in the appropriate column that is closest to the percentage that you are given.

Step 2. Find the *z* score that corresponds to this percentage.

Step 3. If the problem requires that you transform the *z* score to a raw score, then use the following formula to do so.

$$X = z(\sigma) + \mu$$

Example Problem

Tom's exam score is greater than 75% of the scores in his class. If the class mean and standard deviation are 75 and 10, respectively, what is Tom's exam score?

Solution

If Tom's score is greater than 75% of the scores, then it is greater than the scores below the mean, so it is greater than the scores represented by the left half of the normal curve. It is also greater than the next 25% of the scores, so look up "% MEAN TO *z*" = 25% to find the *z* score that corresponds to Tom's score. The *z* score that corresponds to the "% MEAN TO *z*" that is closest to 25.00% is 0.67. (The *z* score is 0.67, because 24.86% is closer than 25.17% to 25%.) Now substitute 0.67 for *z* in the formula that converts a *z* score to a raw score to find Tom's exam score:

$$X = 0.67(10) + 75 = \textbf{81.7}$$

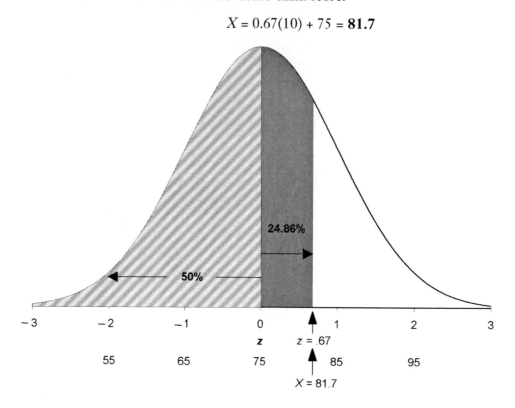

The z Table and Distributions of Means

As noted in the previous graph, sample means may also be converted to *z* statistics and assigned a probability from Table B.1 in the appendix of the text (note that the mean score of 75 correponds to a *z* score of zero). The formula used to convert a sample mean to a *z* statistic is similar to the formula used to convert a raw score to a *z* score. The most frequent error made by students is forgetting to use the standard error instead of the standard deviation in the denominator of the formula for converting a sample mean to a *z* statistic. The formulas are presented next for your convenience:

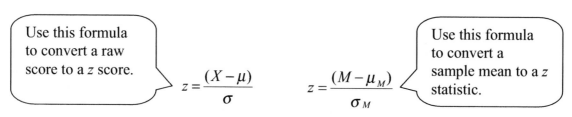

Use this formula to convert a raw score to a *z* score.

$$z = \frac{(X - \mu)}{\sigma}$$

$$z = \frac{(M - \mu_M)}{\sigma_M}$$

Use this formula to convert a sample mean to a *z* statistic.

Example Problem

In a certain population of individuals with fibromyalgia, the distribution of self-ratings of pain on a scale from 0 to 10 is approximately normal, with $\mu = 5.4$ and $\sigma = 3.2$. A sample of 50 individuals selected from this population participated in the second phase of the clinical trials of a new medication developed to relieve the pain associated with this condition. Following treatment, the mean pain rating in this sample was found to be 4.5. Determine the percentage of all samples of 50 individuals selected from this population expected to have a mean no greater than 4.5.

Solution

Convert the sample mean of 4.5 to a *z* statistic.

$$z = \frac{M - \mu_M}{\sigma_M} = \frac{4.5 - 5.4}{3.2 / \sqrt{50}} = \frac{-0.9}{0.453} = -1.99$$

Locate $z = 1.99$ in the left column of Table B.1 in the appendix of the text and find the % IN TAIL value to be **2.33**.

z	% MEAN TO *z*	% IN TAIL
1.95	47.44	2.56
1.96	47.50	2.50
1.97	47.56	2.44
1.98	47.61	2.39
1.99	47.67	2.33
2.00	47.72	2.28

The percentage of all samples of 50 individuals selected from this population who are expected to have a mean no greater than 4.5 is 2.33. We may also express this outcome as the percent chance (2.33), or probability (0.023), of randomly selecting a single sample of 50 individuals from this population and observing a mean less than or equal to 4.5.

> The Assumptions and the Steps of Hypothesis Testing

The Three Assumptions for Conducting Analyses

The process of selecting a statistical test requires that you determine whether the assumptions of the test are violated to a degree that would prohibit its use. The **assumptions** of a statistical analysis "are the characteristics that we ideally require the population from which we are sampling to have so that we can make accurate inferences" (p. 157 in the text). The basic assumptions are as follows:

1. The dependent variable is measured on an interval or ratio scale.
2. The participants are randomly selected from the target population.

3. The values of the dependent variable (scores) are approximately normally distributed in the population.

In the practice of research, all three of these general assumptions are frequently compromised to some degree. For example, psychological variables such as anxiety, guilt, happiness, well-being, depression, extraversion, neuroticism, sensation-seeking, intelligence, attitudes, consideration of future consequences, and so forth are typically measured with paper-and-pencil instruments (scales) that are assumed to yield scores on an interval scale. However, this assumption is rarely, if ever, supported by empirical evidence. The assumption that participants are randomly selected from the population is routinely violated in the behavioral sciences in which convenience, not random, samples tend to be the rule. The cost of violating this assumption is paid in terms of limiting the extent to which the results may be generalized. Results determined for a convenience sample of participants may be generalized only to populations of individuals who are similar to the participants comprising the studied sample. The normality assumption may be ignored for large samples, thanks to the central limit theorem. For smaller samples, most statistical tests are relatively *robust* with respect to violations of this assumption. A statistical test is described as **robust** if the accuracy of the results is not markedly affected by the violation of one or more of its assumptions.

The statistical tests described in Chapters 7–14 are called **parametric tests** because they all assume that the dependent variable values are normally distributed in the population.[1] However, for small samples from populations with a nonnormal distribution, the parametric tests may be inappropriate. Under these conditions one of the **nonparametric tests**, which are required when the dependent variable is measured on a nominal or an ordinal scale, may be used instead of a parametric test. The nonparametric tests have more limited assumptions but in most cases are less sensitive than the parametric tests to the effects of the independent variable. Several of the nonparametric tests, or distribution-free tests as they are sometimes called, are described in Chapter 15.

The Six Steps of Hypothesis Testing

The six steps of hypothesis testing are described on text pages 158–160. The labels for each of these steps are listed next, and the application of the steps to the most basic hypothesis test, the one-sample *z* test, is outlined in the following section.

Step 1. Identify the populations, comparison distribution, and assumptions.

Step 2. State the null and research hypotheses.

---

[1] The term *parametric* refers to the fact that the normal probability distribution is defined by *parameters*, two of which are μ and σ.

Step 3. Determine the characteristics of the comparison distribution.

Step 4. Determine the critical, or cutoff, values of the test statistic.

Step 5. Calculate the test statistic.

Step 6. Make a decision regarding the status of the null hypothesis.

> An Example of the *z* Test

A researcher believes that a new form of psychotherapy will increase the self-esteem scores of persons with low self-esteem. Accordingly, she obtains a sample of 16 individuals with low self-esteem, administers the form of psychotherapy over a six-week period, and evaluates the self-esteem of these clients using a suitably valid and reliable instrument. The researcher computes the mean (M) of the self-esteem scores in this sample of 16 clients and finds it to be 14. This single value is the researcher's best estimate of μ_1, the mean of the population of clients receiving the new psychotherapy. The mean self-esteem score in the population of *untreated* individuals with low self-esteem is known to be **12** ($\mu_2 = 12$), with a standard deviation of **4** ($\sigma = 4$). The question to be addressed by the hypothesis test is thus whether a sample mean of 14 is sufficiently greater than 12 to qualify as evidence that the new form of psychotherapy increases self-esteem in this population. The answer requires a test of the null hypothesis at the 0.05 level of statistical significance, that is, the researcher will reject the null hypothesis if the observed mean happens less than 5% of the time by chance.

Step 1. Describe the populations and the comparison distribution, and make sure that the test is sufficiently robust with respect to any possible violations of its assumptions.

The population specified by the null hypothesis (Population 2) is the population of all persons with low self-esteem who have not been treated with this new form of psychotherapy. The population specified by the research hypothesis (Population 1) is the population of all individuals with low self-esteem who have been treated with the new psychotherapy. The comparison distribution is the distribution of means of all possible samples of 16 scores from Population 2. The one-sample *z* test is selected for this hypothesis test because the population standard deviation is known from prior research. The *z* test is a parametric test, so it requires that the self-esteem scores be measured on an interval or ratio scale and that the scores follow a normal distribution. The sample of clients is not a random sample, so the results may only be generalized to similar individuals.

Step 2. State the null and research hypotheses.

As you learned in Chapter 5, the hypothesis tested in a scientific study is not the researcher's hypothesis. Rather, it is the null hypothesis, a statement that is the logical opposite of the research hypothesis. The term *null* is from the Latin *nullus*, which means "not any." This term is aptly descriptive of the null hypothesis, which always states that there is "not any" effect of the independent variable and thus "not any" difference between the means of two or more populations. In the present example, a statement of the null hypothesis might read this way: "The new form of psychotherapy does *not* increase the self-esteem of persons with low self-esteem." Phrased more formally and in statistical terms, the null hypothesis states that "The mean score on a measure of self-esteem in the population of individuals with low self-esteem who are treated with this new form of psychotherapy is not higher than the mean self-esteem score in the population of individuals with low self-esteem who are not treated."

In symbols: $H_0: \mu_1 \leq \mu_2$.

where,

H_0 refers to the null hypothesis

μ_1 refers to the mean self-esteem score in the population of persons with low self-esteem treated with a new form of psychotherapy

μ_2 refers to the mean self-esteem score in the population of persons with low self-esteem who are not treated with the new form of psychotherapy

The research, or alternative, hypothesis may read as follows: "Psychotherapy increases the self-esteem of persons with low self-esteem." In more formal terms, "The mean score on a measure of self-esteem is higher in the population of individuals with low self-esteem who are treated with a new form of psychotherapy than in the population of individuals with low self-esteem who are not treated." In symbols: $H_1: \mu_1 > \mu_2$. Note the contrast between the symbolic expressions of the null and research hypotheses:

$$H_0: \mu_1 \leq \mu_2$$
$$H_1: \mu_1 > \mu_2$$

The statement of the research hypothesis is a *directional* statement, because it declares that the new form of psychotherapy has a directional effect—that is, it increases levels of self-esteem. A directional statement of the research hypothesis requires a **one-tailed** test of the null hypothesis. A one-tailed test permits the rejection of the null hypothesis if the sample outcome is sufficiently extreme in the direction, or tail of the comparison distribution, predicted by the research hypothesis. A **two-tailed test** is required by a *nondirectional* null hypothesis: $\mu_1 = \mu_2$. A two-tailed test is so-named because it permits the rejection of the null hypothesis if the sample outcome is sufficiently extreme in either tail of the comparison distribution. A two-tailed test is more conservative (makes it more difficult to reject the null hypothesis) and for this reason is encountered more frequently in the literature of the behavioral sciences. We will work through this problem as both a one-tailed and two-tailed test for illustration purposes.

Step 3. Determine the characteristics of the comparison distribution.

The comparison distribution is the distribution of means of all possible samples of 16 scores from Population 2, the population specified by the null hypothesis. According to the null hypothesis, the new form of psychotherapy is without effect, so the mean of the population of individuals with low self-esteem who receive the new form of therapy is the same as the mean of the population of *untreated* individuals with low self-esteem. For the purpose of this example of hypothesis testing, we will assume that the mean of the population of untreated individuals with low esteem is known to be 12 ($\mu_2 = 12$), with a standard deviation of 4 ($\sigma = 4$). The mean of the comparison distribution is the same as the mean of the population of self-esteem scores specified by the null hypothesis:

$$\mu_M = \mu_2 = 12$$

The standard deviation of the comparison distribution (the standard error) is the population standard deviation divided by the square root of the sample size:

$$\sigma_M = \frac{\sigma}{\sqrt{N}} = \frac{4}{\sqrt{16}} = \frac{4}{4} = 1$$

The shape of the comparison distribution is normal, because we are assuming that self-esteem scores are normally distributed in the population. In actual research, we would need some evidence to support this assumption. Given the widespread belief among psychologists that most psychological and physical variables are normally distributed, this is a credible assumption. However, it is not a trivial assumption. Assuming a normal distribution of self-esteem scores in the population, the comparison distribution is also a normal distribution and may be sketched as follows:

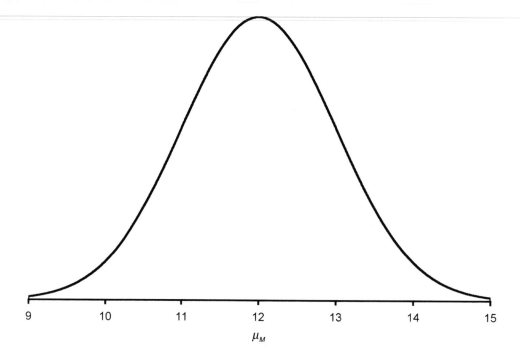

The null hypothesis is assumed to be true and the "burden of proof" is on the researcher to show that this is not a reasonable assumption. The researcher accepts this burden of proof by agreeing to test the null hypothesis at the 0.05 *p* level.

Step 5. Determine the critical values of the test statistic.

The **critical values** of the test statistic (*z* in this example) are determined by the level of statistical significance, called the *p* level. The ***p* level** provides an answer to the question: How unusual or extreme must a sample mean be before the null hypothesized value of *µ* is rejected as implausible? If a sample mean has a probability of occurrence that is less than or equal to the *p* level, then the null hypothesis is considered to be implausible and may be rejected as such. The most commonly used *p* level is 0.05 (5%), so we will use this *p* level as well. In Table B.1 in the text, look up the percentage in the "% IN TAIL" column that is closest to the *p* level (5%, in this example). Two values, 4.95% and 5.05%, are equidistant from 5%, so the critical value of *z* is 1.645, the value midway between 1.64 and 1.65. The research hypothesis states that the mean self-esteem score in the population of treated individuals is greater than the mean of the population of untreated individuals, so the **critical value** of *z* is 1.645 instead of –1.645. The positive value is chosen because it defines ("cuts off") the *rejection region* of the comparison distribution. The upper tail of the comparison distribution is called the **critical region** (this is often called a "rejection region"), because a sample mean that falls in this region will permit a rejection of the null hypothesis. If the researcher hypothesis stated that the mean of the population of treated individuals is *less than* the mean of the population of untreated individuals (i.e., $\mu_1 < \mu_2$), then the rejection region would be the *lower* 5% of the comparison distribution, and the critical value of z would be -1.645. The comparison distribution, with rejection region, looks like this:

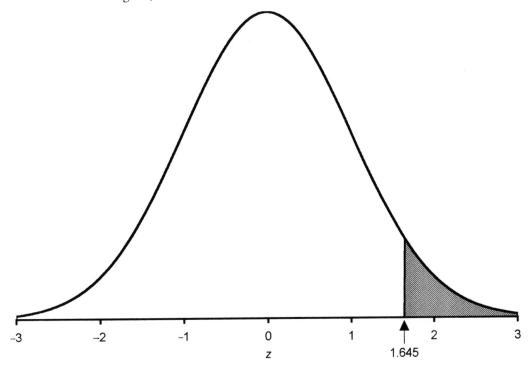

If this had been a *two*-tailed test, the critical values of the z statistic would have been determined by dividing the p level by 2 (0.05 / 2 = 0.025). From Table B.1 in the text, the z statistics that cut off the upper and lower 2.5% of the area under the comparison distribution are 1.96 and -1.96. This is why the two-tailed test is more conservative; it is easier to reject the null hypothesis when the critical value is 1.645 than when the critical value is farther out into the tails at 1.96.

Step 6. Convert the sample mean to a z statistic.

$$z = \frac{M - \mu_M}{\sigma_M} = \frac{M - \mu_M}{\sigma / \sqrt{N}} = \frac{14 - 12}{4 / \sqrt{16}} = \frac{2}{4/4} = 2$$

In hypothesis testing, z is called a **test statistic**. It is necessary to convert the sample mean to a z statistic, because Table B.1 in the text provides percentages that correspond to values of z rather than sample means.

Step 7. Make a decision regarding the null hypothesis.

The null hypothesis should be rejected because the computed z statistic (z = 2) is more extreme than the critical value of z (1.645). This is true for either the one-tailed or the two-tailed test (z of 2 exceeded the cutoffs of 1.645 and 1.96 respectively). Put another way, the null hypothesis may be rejected because the computed value of z falls in the critical or rejection region. Having rejected the null hypothesis, we may conclude that the new form of psychotherapy appears to increase self-esteem in the population of individuals who are similar to the clients tested in this study.

Note that the *decision* is always to either *reject* or *fail to reject* the *null* hypothesis. The *conclusion* is that the sample evidence supports or does not support the *research* hypothesis. It is inappropriate to "accept," or "conclude support for," the null hypothesis. In addition, you should never use any forms of the words "prove" or "true" when interpreting the results of a hypothesis test. The results either "support" or "do not support" the research hypothesis.

When the null hypothesis is rejected, the sample outcome is typically described as **statistically significant**. In hypothesis testing, *significant* means *unlikely to have occurred by chance*; it does not mean *important*. A sample outcome that results in a failure to reject the null hypothesis is a *nonsignificant* result.

STUDY QUESTIONS

1. The table of normal curve percentages in the appendix of the text lists z scores in one column and the percentage of scores _____ in the second column.
   a. between any pair of z scores
   b. less than or equal to each z score
   c. greater than or equal to each z score
   d. between the mean ($z = 0$) and each z score

2. The percentage of scores between $z = -1.14$ and $z = +0.67$ on the standard normal curve is:
   a. 46.49.
   b. 37.85.
   c. 12.43.
   d. 62.15.

3. In a certain population, the distribution of height follows the normal curve, with a mean of 5 feet 8 inches (68 inches) and a standard deviation of 3 inches. What is the percentile rank of an individual who is 6 feet (72 inches) tall?
   a. 90.82
   b. 9.18
   c. 69.74
   d. 30.26

4. In a certain population, the distribution of height follows the normal curve, with a mean of 5 feet 8 inches (68 inches) and a standard deviation of 3 inches. What is the percentile rank of an individual who is 5 feet (60 inches) tall?
   a. 0.38
   b. 99.62
   c. 68.75
   d. 31.25

5. In a certain population, the distribution of height follows the normal curve, with a mean of 5 feet 8 inches (68 inches) and a standard deviation of 3 inches. Determine the percentage of individuals in this population who are between 5 feet 6 inches and 5 feet 10 inches tall.
   a. 68.26
   b. 97.72
   c. 68.75
   d. 49.71

6. Kate's score on a chemistry exam is 62. If the scores on this exam are approximately normally distributed with a mean and standard deviation of 71 and 9, respectively, what is the percentile rank of Kate's score?
   a. 84.13
   b. 73.79
   c. 62
   d. 15.87

7. One of the tools used to diagnose mental retardation (MR) is the Wechsler IQ test, which yields scores that are approximately normally distributed with a mean of 100 and a standard deviation of 15. Approximately 85% of persons with MR are considered mildly retarded and have IQ scores ranging between 50 and 70. What is the percentile rank of an IQ score of 50?
   a. 4
   b. 0.04
   c. 0.96
   d. 96.96

8. One of the tools used to diagnose mental retardation (MR) is the Wechsler IQ test, which yields scores that are approximately normally distributed with a mean of 100 and a standard deviation of 15. Approximately 85% of persons with MR are considered mildly retarded and have IQ scores ranging between 50 and 70. What is the percentile rank of an IQ score of 70?
   a. 97.72
   b. 2.28
   c. 85
   d. 15

9. One of the tools used to diagnose mental retardation (MR) is the Wechsler IQ test, which yields scores that are approximately normally distributed with a mean of 100 and a standard deviation of 15. Approximately 85% of persons with MR are considered mildly retarded and have IQ scores ranging between 50 and 70. Approximately what percentage of all IQ scores are between 50 and 70?
   a. 85
   b. 20
   c. 2.23
   d. 1.33

10. Scores on a certain mathematics achievement test are known to be normally distributed with a mean of 75 and a standard deviation of 12. If a minimum score of 90 is needed to qualify for membership in a high school math club, what percentage of the students taking this test are expected to qualify for membership?
   a. 2.5
   b. 1.25
   c. 10.57
   d. 89.44

11. A qualification for membership in the high-IQ society Mensa is an IQ score at the 98th percentile. If IQ test scores are normally distributed with a mean of 100 and a standard deviation of 15, what is the minimum score needed to qualify for membership?
    a. 144
    b. 169
    c. 131
    d. 123

12. A local pizzeria claims that it delivers its pizzas to any location within a 15-mile radius within an average of 30 minutes, with a standard deviation of 12 minutes. Suppose that a researcher working for a competitor orders 16 pizzas to be delivered to different locations within a 15-mile radius, and computes a sample mean delivery time of 38 minutes. Which one of the following is the *most* appropriate conclusion from this study?
    a. The research hypothesis is supported; the mean delivery time for this pizzeria is greater than 30 minutes.
    b. The research hypothesis is not supported; the mean delivery time for this pizzeria is fewer than or equal to 30 minutes.
    c. The research hypothesis is not supported; the mean delivery time for this pizzeria is 30 minutes.
    d. The research hypothesis is supported; the mean delivery time for this pizza chain is fewer than 30 minutes.

13. The scores on a certain psychological test are known to be skewed with a mean of 62 and a standard deviation of 18. What is the probability that a sample of 50 scores randomly selected from this population will have a mean of 68 or more?
    a. < 0.01
    b. 0.37
    c. 0.63
    d. 0.99

14. Parametric analysis procedures such as the *z* test require that participants are sampled randomly from a population in which the values of the dependent variable are measured on an interval scale and are approximately normally distributed. Such requirements are called:
    a. ethical guidelines.
    b. assumptions.
    c. research protocol.
    d. critical values.

15. Statistical analyses based on a set of assumptions about the population are:
    a. described as robust.
    b. called parametric tests.
    c. called nonparametric tests.
    d. conducted less frequently than analyses that are not based on any assumptions.

16. A **robust** hypothesis test is one that:
    a. frequently results in a rejection of the null hypothesis.
    b. is relatively free of assumptions about the shape of the distribution of scores in the sample.
    c. is relatively free of assumptions about the shape of the distribution of scores in the population.
    d. produces reasonably accurate results even when some its assumptions are not met.

17. Which one of the following is *most* clearly an example of a null hypothesis? (*Hint: null* is from the Latin *nullus* which means "not any" as in "not any" effect of the experimental treatment and thus "not any" difference between two populations.)
    a. Most people cry when they are extremely happy.
    b. People who have and who have not previously used marijuana are equally likely to be regular users of "hard drugs" such as cocaine and heroin.
    c. Actors who have received training in "method acting" will get more roles than actors who have not received such training.
    d. Children who were physically abused by their parents are more likely to physically abuse their own children.

18. Which one of the following is *most* clearly an example of a research hypothesis?
    a. College graduates do not work a 40-hour week as is typical of the general population.
    b. CEO's have the same average cholesterol levels as the general population.
    c. The new drug is no more effective than the standard treatment.
    d. The new treatment has no effect on the cure rate.

19. The **critical values** are the:
    a. sample scores that are obtained if the null hypothesis is true.
    b. sample scores that are obtained if the null hypothesis is false.
    c. values of the test statistic that the computed values of the test statistic must exceed in order to reject the null hypothesis.
    d. values of the test statistic that the computed values of the test statistic must exceed in order to accept the null hypothesis.

20. The *cutoff score* on the comparison distribution is a score that is so extreme that it has only a 5% chance (or less) of occurring if the null hypothesis is true. In this example, "5%" is a:
    a. critical value.
    b. *p* level.
    c. statistically significant statistic.
    d. sample score.

21. A researcher predicted that an experimental treatment would alter participants' scores on a certain dependent variable. If the critical value of the *z* statistic is 1.96, and the computed value of the *z* statistic is 1.59, then this researcher should conclude that the results:
    a. do not support the null hypothesis.
    b. support the null hypothesis.
    c. support the research hypothesis.
    d. are not statistically significant.

22. In a study using 0.05 as the *p* level, a **statistically significant** finding is one that:
    a. has a probability of occurrence that is less than 5%, if the null hypothesis is true.
    b. has a probability of occurrence that is less than 5%, if the null hypothesis is false.
    c. is expected to occur by chance and thus requires that we fail to reject the null hypothesis.
    d. is so extreme that it results in the rejection of the research hypothesis.

23. A clinical psychologist hypothesized that women who have been physically abused by their husbands will score higher on a test of loyalty than women who have not been physically abused. If the population of physically abused women is labeled "Population 1," which one of the following is the null hypothesis to be tested by this psychologist?
    a. $\mu_1 < \mu_2$
    b. $\mu_1 \geq \mu_2$
    c. $\mu_1 \neq \mu_2$
    d. $\mu_1 = \mu_2$

24. Which one of the following statements requires a **one-tailed test** of the null hypothesis?
    a. Winning a one million dollar lottery will increase a person's relative happiness.
    b. Infants who receive special training will learn to walk at the same time as infants who do receive any special training.
    c. College graduates do not work a 40-hour work week as is typical of the general population.
    d. Compared to mice treated with a placebo, mice that receive daily injections of nicotine for a period of five weeks will show a different level of activity when both groups are injected with a stimulant drug.

25. The distribution of scores on the Beck Depression Inventory II following four weeks of a standard therapy in a certain population of outpatients is known to be normally distributed with mean (μ) = 27.82 and standard deviation (σ) = 9.55. A researcher believes that the distribution of depression scores following four weeks of a new therapy differs from the distribution of scores obtained following the standard therapy. If Population 1 is the population of depression scores following four weeks of the new therapy, which one of the following is the null hypothesis being tested?
    a. $\mu_1 < \mu_2$
    b. $\mu_1 > \mu_2$
    c. $\mu_1 = \mu_2$
    d. $\mu_1 \geq \mu_2$

26. A sample mean that is 2 standard errors below the mean of a comparison distribution of means has a(n) _____ probability of having been selected from the null-hypothesized population.
    a. low (< 0.05)
    b. medium (around 0.5)
    c. high (> 0.95)
    d. unknown

27. When conducting a **two-tailed test** of the null hypothesis at the 0.05 *p* level, the critical values of the *z* statistic are _____.
    a. −2.58 and +2.58
    b. −2.33 and +2.33
    c. −1.96 and +1.96
    d. −1.645 and +1.645

28. A school psychologist is convinced that the mean IQ score of the high school seniors in her district is different than 100. Accordingly, she administered an IQ test to a random sample of 50 seniors in her district and determined the mean IQ score for her sample to be 104. Assume that IQ scores are normally distributed in the population with a mean of 100 and a standard deviation of 15. What is the critical value of the *z* statistic for this test of the null hypothesis?
    a. 1.645
    b. 1.96 and −1.96
    c. −1.645
    d. −1.96 only

29. A school psychologist is convinced that the mean IQ score of the high school seniors in her district is different than 100. Accordingly, she administered an IQ test to a random sample of 50 seniors in her district and determined the mean IQ score for her sample to be 104. Assume that IQ scores are normally distributed in the population with a mean of 100 and a standard deviation of 15. What is the computed value of the z statistic that this psychologist will use to test the null hypothesis?
    a. 0.27
    b. 0.04
    c. 1.89
    d. 13.33

30. The distribution of scores on the Beck Depression Inventory II following four weeks of a standard therapy in a certain population of outpatients is normally distributed with mean $(\mu) = 27.82$ and standard deviation $(\sigma) = 9.55$. A researcher hypothesized that the mean depression score following four weeks of a new therapy differs from the mean depression score following four weeks of the standard therapy. Suppose that the mean score for a sample of 36 patients following four weeks of the new therapy is 24.38. Which of the following is the most appropriate conclusion?
    a. Reject the null hypothesis because the computed z statistic is more extreme than the critical value of the z statistic, -1.645.
    b. Fail to reject the null hypothesis because the computed z statistic is not more extreme than the critical value of the z statistic, -1.645.
    c. Reject the null hypothesis because the computed z statistic is more extreme than the critical value of the z statistic, -1.96.
    d. Fail to reject the null hypothesis because the computed z statistic is not more extreme than the critical value of the z statistic, -1.96.

31. A school psychologist is convinced that the mean IQ score of the high school seniors in her district is different from the standard mean IQ, 100. Accordingly, she administered an IQ test to a random sample of 50 seniors in her district and determined the mean IQ score for her sample to be 104. Assume that IQ scores are normally distributed in the population with a mean of 100 and a standard deviation of 15. Assume also that the computed value of the z statistic is in the critical region. Which one of the following is the appropriate decision regarding the null hypothesis?
    a. The null hypothesis is proven to be true.
    b. The null hypothesis is proven to be false.
    c. The null hypothesis is not rejected.
    d. The null hypothesis is rejected.

32. A researcher predicted that an experimental treatment would alter participants' scores on a certain dependent variable. If the critical value of the z statistic is 1.96, and the computed value of the z statistic is 2.07, then this researcher should conclude that the results:

    a. prove that the research hypothesis is true.
    b. prove that the null hypothesis is true.
    c. are inconclusive.
    d. support the research hypothesis.

ANSWERS TO CHAPTER 7 STUDY QUESTIONS

Question Number	Correct Answer	Question Number	Correct Answer
1	d, p. 149	14	b, p. 157
2	d, pp. 149–154	15	b, p. 157
3	a, pp. 149–154	16	d, p. 158
4	a, pp. 149–154	17	b, p. 159 (Choice b is the only statement of no difference between two populations.)
5	a, pp. 149–154		
6	d, pp. 149–154		
7	b, pp. 149–154	18	a, p. 159 (Choice a is the only statement declaring a difference between two populations.)
8	b, pp. 149–154		
9	c, pp. 149–154		
10	c, pp. 154–155	19	c, p. 159
11	c, pp. 154–155 (Locate the percentage in the "% IN TAIL" column that is closest to 2 and find it to be 2.02. The corresponding value of *z* is 2.05, indicating that a score at the 98th percentile is 2.05 standard deviations above the mean. So, 2.05(15) + 100 = 130.75, the minimum IQ score required for Mensa membership.)	20	b, p. 159
		21	d, pp. 159–160
		22	a, p. 160
		23	c, p. 163
		24	a, p. 163
		25	c, p. 163
		26	a, p. 164 [This is a very basic question about probabilities (*p* values) and *z* statistics; note that the cutoff *z* statistics for the 0.05 level of significance in a two-tailed test are 1.96 standard errors from the mean in either direction, so a sample mean that is 2 standard errors from the mean of the comparison distribution would be labeled "statistically significant" because the *p* value is less than 0.025.]
12	a, pp. 155–160 (The computed *z* statistic = 2.67, and the critical *z* statistic is 1.645. Note that choice b is a statement of support for the null hypothesis, whereas choices c and d are statements of support for incorrect variations of the null hypothesis. The logic of hypothesis testing does not permit a conclusion of support for the null hypothesis.)		
		27	c, p. 164
13	a, pp. 155–156 [The sample size is sufficiently large to use the normal curve percentages. Compute $z = (68 - 62) / (18 / \sqrt{50}) = 2.35$, then look up $z = 2.35$ in a table of normal curve percentages and find "% IN TAIL" to be 0.94%. The probability of observing a sample mean of 68 or more from a distribution of means of samples of $N = 50$ from the population described is 0.0094.]	28	b, p. 164 (The research hypothesis is nondirectional, so a one-tailed test is required. The critical value of the *z* statistic defines, or cuts off, the most extreme 2.5% of the area in the right, or upper, tail of the comparison distribution and the left, or lower, tail.)
		29	c, pp. 155 and 164
		30	d, p. 165
		31	d, p. 165
		32	d, p. 165

CHAPTER EIGHT

Confidence Intervals, Effect Size, and Statistical Power

CHAPTER OUTLINE

Confidence Intervals
- Interval Estimates
- Calculating Confidence Intervals with z Distributions

Effect Size and p_{rep}
- The Effect of Sample Size on Statistical Significance
- What Effect Size Is
- Cohen's d
- p_{rep}

Statistical Power
- The Importance of Statistical Power
- Three Factors that Affect Statistical Power

LEARNING OBJECTIVES

After studying this chapter, you should be able to:

1. Define each of the following terms and provide examples that are not in the text: *point estimate, interval estimate, confidence interval, effect size, Cohen's d, p_{rep}, statistical power, alpha, Institutional Review Board (IRB), meta-analysis,* and *file drawer statistic.*

2. Distinguish between *statistical significance* and *practical importance* and discuss this distinction with regard to the issue of gender differences in mathematics reasoning ability.

3. Discuss the concept of *confidence intervals* as an estimation procedure as well as an alternative to traditional hypothesis testing. Include in your discussion references to point and interval estimates and relate the level of confidence to the p level used in hypothesis testing.

4. Explain the relation between a confidence interval and the phrase "margin of error" that frequently accompanies media reports of political poll results.

5. Calculate a 95% confidence interval for a z test.

6. Discuss the concept of *effect size* and include in your discussion a distinction between the *size* of an effect and the *statistical significance* of an effect. In addition, you should know how to compute effect size statistics for *z* tests (Cohen's *d* statistic).

7. Explain p_{rep} and be able to calculate it using Microsoft Excel.

8. Discuss the concept of *statistical power*, including its (a) formal definition, (b) relation to the probability of committing a Type I error; (c) calculation for a *z* test; and (d) susceptibility to the influence of effect size (as determined by the difference between population means as well as the size of the population standard deviation), sample size, alpha (the *p* level), and one-tailed vs. two-tailed tests.

CHAPTER REVIEW

> Confidence Intervals

You were introduced to the six steps of hypothesis testing in Chapter 7. Recall that the most basic hypothesis test, a *z* test, involved converting a sample mean to a *z* statistic to determine the probability of observing a sample mean as extreme as the one observed under the assumption that the null hypothesis is true. The *z* test provided an answer to the question, "What is the probability of observing a sample mean at least this extreme if the population mean is the value specified by the null hypothesis?" If the *z* statistic was associated with a probability (*p* value) less than or equal to the *p* level (usually 0.05), then the null hypothesis was rejected. More specifically, the null hypothesized value of the population mean was rejected as the true value of the mean of the population represented by the sample.

The sample mean is termed a **point estimate**, because it may be located as a point on the scale used to measure the dependent variable. To quote the text, a point estimate is "just one number used as an estimate of the population parameter" (p. 177). Of course, the researcher knows that she would almost certainly compute a different sample mean each time she selected a sample from this population, so each use of the sample mean as a point estimate of the population mean is accompanied by error. In Chapter 7, you learned that the comparison distribution of sample means is the distribution of all possible means of samples of a given size (denoted by N) from the population of interest. You also learned that the mean of the distribution of sample means (μ_M) is equal to the mean of the population (μ) and you learned to calculate the standard error (σ_M) as the standard deviation of this distribution of sample means. Now, perhaps it is easier to see why the standard error is conceptualized as an "error"; it is a measure of error associated with using the sample mean as a point estimate of the population mean.

Interval Estimates

To improve on the point estimate, the researcher could accompany the sample mean with the standard error and thereby provide an **interval estimate** of the unknown value of the population mean. She could report, for example, that her best estimate of the population mean is given by the interval $M \pm \sigma_M$. From Chapter 7, you know that approximately 68% of the sample means in the comparison distribution are within 1 standard error of the population mean. This means that the interval $M \pm \sigma_M$ will include the unknown value of the population mean in about 68% of the samples from the population. This is not the same as saying that there is a 68% chance that any one particular interval includes the population mean. The population mean is a fixed value, so it is either in a given interval or it isn't. The thing that varies from sample to sample is the interval, not the population mean. So, instead of saying that there is about a 68% chance that any specific $M \pm \sigma_M$ interval includes the population mean, we would say that 68% of all $M \pm \sigma_M$ intervals derived from samples of this size from this population will include the population mean. The idea of an interval estimate is just like the margin of error reported for political polls.

Calculating Confidence Intervals with z Distributions

Why limit ourselves to an interval that will include ("cover" or "trap") the population mean just 68% of the time? To increase our confidence that the interval constructed around the sample mean includes the population mean, we could extend the interval an additional standard error in each direction. Now, we could say that roughly 95% of the intervals that extend from $M - 2\sigma_M$ to $M + 2\sigma_M$ will include the population mean. This is, in fact, the convention adopted by statisticians and researchers, with one small adjustment. The level of confidence is specified to be exactly, rather than approximately, 95%. And the interval is, appropriately enough, called a **confidence interval**. To make the interval a 95% confidence interval, the standard error is multiplied by 1.96 instead of 2. You may recall from Chapter 7 that 1.96 and –1.96 were introduced as the critical values of z that define, or "cut off," the upper and lower 2.5% of the sample means in the comparison distribution. The values +1.96 and –1.96 are thus the critical values of z for a two-tailed test of any null hypothesis conducted at a p level of 0.05. This means that a given level of confidence is the additive inverse of the p level used in traditional hypothesis testing. For the frequently used p level of 0.05 (5%),

$$\text{Level of confidence} = 100\% - p \text{ level} = 100\% - 5\% = 95\%$$

So now, instead of testing a single null-hypothesized value of the population mean, you can construct an interval using a sampling procedure that includes the actual value of the population mean 95% of the time. The upshot is this: Any null-hypothesized value of the population mean that is *not* within a given confidence interval may be rejected at the 0.05 p level.

In constructing a 95% confidence interval, you are in effect saying the following: "I know that the chances are not good that my sample mean will have the same value as the true population mean. I am simply using my sample mean as an *estimate* of the true value of population mean. However, if I construct a 95% confidence interval around my sample mean, I will have an interval that was produced by a sampling procedure that includes the true, but unknown, value of the population mean 95% of the time. I am 95% confident because the interval will extend exactly 1.96 standard errors above and below my sample mean, and for all normal distributions of sample means, 95% of the means are within 1.96 standard errors of the center of the distribution."

Here is an example. You (for this exercise you are a licensed clinical psychologist) may think that the IQ of the average college student is higher than 100, the scale score identified as the average IQ score in the general population. The standard deviation is arbitrarily assigned to be 15 on the Wechsler Adult Intelligence Scale (WAIS) and 16 on the Stanford-Binet IQ test. We'll use the WAIS value of 15 as the population standard deviation, that is, $\sigma = 15$. So, rather than test the null hypothesis which states that the IQ of the average college student is the same as the mean IQ in the general population ($\mu_{College\ Students} = \mu_{General\ Population} = 100$), you decide to gather a sample of 36 college students, administer the WAIS to them, compute the sample mean IQ score, and use this sample mean to construct a 95% confidence interval.

You compute the sample mean IQ score and find that it is 109—i.e., $M = 109$. Now you are ready to construct the limits of a 95% confidence interval.

1. Compute the standard error of the mean (the standard deviation of the comparison distribution of sample means). This is the population standard deviation (15) divided by the square root of the sample size (36). So, the standard error (σ_M) is 15 / 6 = 2.5.

2. You are constructing a 95% confidence interval, so the values of z are −1.96 and +1.96. (For a 90% confidence interval, the two z values would be −1.645 and +1.645; for a 99% confidence interval, the two values of z would be −2.58 and +2.58.)

3. The upper limit of the confidence interval is $1.96(\sigma_M) + M$; thus,

$$M_{Upper} = 1.96(2.5) + 109 = 4.9 + 109 = 113.9.$$

4. The lower limit of the confidence interval is $-1.96(\sigma_M) + M$; thus,

$$M_{Lower} = -1.96(2.5) + 109 = -4.9 + 109 = 104.1.$$

If the value of the population mean specified by the null hypothesis (100) is within the CI, then the null hypothesis may *not* be rejected. In this example, however, the null hypothesis may be rejected, because 100 is not within the limits of the confidence interval. Neither is 115, nor 95, nor 120, nor 102, within the interval, so we may reject all of these values as well, if they were specified by other null hypotheses. Being able to simultaneously reject a large number of null-hypothesized values of a population parameter is an advantage of using a confidence interval over traditional hypothesis testing.

The level of confidence in any particular interval estimate is based on the long-run relative frequency interpretation of probability. More specifically, to say that we are 95% confident that a given interval includes the true value of the mean IQ score in the population of college students is to say that 95% of the confidence intervals constructed from samples of this size from this population include the true value of the population mean. This is worth repeating: If a very large number of studies were conducted just as this one was, and a 95% confidence interval were constructed for each sample, then about 95% of these confidence intervals would include the value of the population mean. One more time: For 95% of all samples of this size that are selected in this way, the interval from 1.96 standard errors below the sample mean to 1.96 standard errors above the sample mean will include the population mean.

To review a point made earlier, please note that it is incorrect to state the probability is 0.95 that any specific confidence interval contains the true value of the population mean. The population parameter is a fixed value and does not vary from sample-to-sample as the confidence interval does. Each time we sample from a population and construct a confidence interval based on a new sample mean, the limits of the interval change. It should be clear that different intervals could not all have the same probability of including the population mean. Any correct probability statement must refer to the sampling process, not to any one interval. The level of confidence we have in any one interval is based on a very large number of repetitions of the sampling process. For a 95% confidence interval, this *process* has a 0.95 probability of producing an interval that will include the true value of the population mean. In other words, if this sampling process were repeated *a very large number of times*, each time resulting in a new mean around which is constructed a new confidence interval, then we can say (with confidence) that *approximately* 95% of these confidence intervals will include the true value of the population mean. If this sampling process were repeated *an infinitely large number of times*, then *exactly* 95% of the confidence intervals constructed as this one was would include the true value of the population mean.

> Effect Size and p_{rep}

Hypothesis testing allows us to assess the statistical significance of a result. However it is also important to assess whether or not the result really makes a difference in terms of the variable being assessed, or whether it really matters in terms of real-world application. Effect size and p_{rep} are two ways to assess the importance of statistical observations.

The Effect of Sample Size on Statistical Significance

Increases in sample size are reflected in the denominator of the standard error equation.

$$\sigma_M = \frac{\sigma}{\sqrt{N}}$$

When a numerator is divided by larger and larger denominators, the result gets smaller and smaller. We saw this in the text when the standard deviation of a population, $\sigma = 99$, was divided by samples of increasing sizes (from 90, 200, 1000 up to 100,000), resulting in increasingly smaller standard error calculations. The impact of sample size is then seen in the z-statistic calculation. In this case, standard error is in the denominator of the equation. When a numerator is divided by a smaller and smaller denominator, the result gets bigger and bigger. Thus, as sample size increases and standard error gets smaller, the z statistic will then get larger.

$$z = \frac{(M - \mu_M)}{\sigma_M}$$

In this way, sample size directly affects the statistical significance of an analysis.

A research outcome that is *statistically significant* may be of substantial or very limited *practical importance*. A statistically significant difference between two sample means (e.g., a gender difference between the mean scores on a standardized test of math reasoning ability) is simply a difference that has a very low probability of having occurred by chance. However, the difference may be so small as to be of almost no practical importance. Benbow and Stanley (1980) found a statistically significant difference in mean scores on the quantitative subtest of the SAT in a sample of approximately 10,000 male and female students in the 7th through the 10th grades who were tested as part of a national talent search (for a more complete discussion, see pp. 176–177 in the text). A sample size this large virtually guarantees that even a tiny difference between the mean scores in the samples of male and female students will be found to be statistically significant. So, do not assume that a result labeled "statistically significant" is also high in practical significance. Such results may, or may not, be noteworthy in terms of informing policy decisions.

What Effect Size Is and Cohen's d

An **effect size** "indicates the size of a difference and is unaffected by sample size" (p. 183). Cohen's *d* is a statistic commonly used as a measure of effect size for studies in which a z test is used to test the null hypothesis. In these studies, effect size refers to the capacity of an experimental treatment (independent variable manipulation) to separate two population means. Because the mean of the population described by the null hypothesis is the only "known" population mean, the mean of the alternative (research) population must be estimated from the sample mean. So, for studies in which the null hypothesis is tested with a z test, Cohen's d is a measure of the number of standard deviations separating the sample mean from the null-hypothesized population mean:

$$d = \frac{M - \mu}{\sigma}$$

To return to the previous example in which you (as a licensed clinical psychologist) hypothesized that the mean IQ in the population of college students differs from the mean IQ in the general population, Cohen's d would be computed as follows:

$$d = \frac{109 - 100}{15} = \frac{9}{15} = \frac{3}{5} = 0.6$$

The overlap between the populations of IQ scores represented by the null and research hypotheses as just described is shown in the following figure:

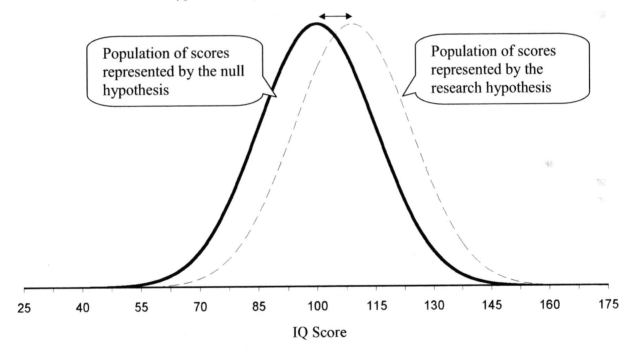

Population of scores represented by the null hypothesis

Population of scores represented by the research hypothesis

| 25 | 40 | 55 | 70 | 85 | 100 | 115 | 130 | 145 | 160 | 175 |

IQ Score

According to the guidelines originally proposed by Cohen (1969, 1977, 1988), this estimated difference of 0.6 standard deviations between the population means is just a bit above a medium effect size, as shown in Table 8-1 in the text:

TABLE 8-1.   COHEN'S CONVENTIONS FOR EFFECT SIZES: *d*

Jacob Cohen has published guidelines (or conventions), based on the overlap between two distributions, to help researchers determine whether an effect is small, medium, or large. These numbers are not cutoffs, merely rough guidelines to aid researchers in their interpretation of results.

EFFECT SIZE	CONVENTION	OVERLAP
Small	0.2	85%
Medium	0.5	67%
Large	0.8	53%

Notice that, because the estimated difference between the population means is measured in terms of the population standard deviation, effect size is completely independent of sample size. This means, of course, that you cannot increase the size of an effect by increasing the number of participants. On the other hand, you *can* increase the likelihood of obtaining a statistically significant result by increasing the number of participants in your study. Recall that the Benbow and Stanley (1980) report of a statistically significant gender difference in mathematics reasoning ability (measured by scores on the math section of the SAT; SAT-M) was based on a sample size of approximately 10,000 students. Given this sample size, a gender difference as small as 3.23 points on the SAT-M would have been statistically significant at the 0.05 *p* level. A "gender gap" this small would translate to an effect size of *d* = 0.04. It is important to note here that there is substantial overlap between populations separated by even large effect sizes (see the above table).

p_{rep}

p_{rep} is the "probability of replicating an effect given a particular population and sample size" (text page 187). In other words, if we run this study again on the same population, sampling the same number of people, what percent of the time can we expect to get the same result? This statistic is preferred over a simple *p* value.

To calculate p_{rep}, a simple command is used in Microsoft Excel (see page 187 or below for the command). First you need to know the exact probability of the test statistic. We find the probability by looking up the percent from the *z* statistic to the tail of the distribution, and we then double that value for two-tailed tests. That number represents the actual *p* level. Now input that value, as a proportion, in the Excel command.

In the example reviewed in the text, the *z* statistic was small at –0.26. This measure was associated with a rather high *p* level, 0.7948 (0.3974 × 2 for the two separate tails). That *p* level resulted in a modest value of p_{rep}, 28.03%. Let's watch how things change with a larger *z* statistic, 2.2. This *z* statistic has

1.39% in the tail. For a two-tailed test, we double the figure to 2.78% or 0.0278, the *p* level for the statistic. We enter in Excel

=NORMSDIST(NORMSINV)((1-.0278)/(SQRT(2)))

and get .9120 as the output. This means that we can expect this result to replicate 91.2% of the time, given the same population and sample size.

> Statistical Power

The results of a study based on a medium-to-large effect size can fail to be significant. Why? The answer is found by examining the statistical power of the study. **Statistical power** is the probability of rejecting a false null hypothesis. In other words, power is the proportion of times a false null hypothesis will be rejected in replications of a study designed to test that hypothesis. Research convention sets 80%, or 0.80, as the minimum power required to run a study. It is in every researcher's interest to maximize the statistical power of each test of a false null hypothesis, just as it is in her or his interest to minimize the opposite probability—that of failing to reject a false null hypothesis—a Type II error. Power is thus the additive inverse of the probability of committing a Type II error. The four possible outcomes of a hypothesis test may be compared in the following decision matrix:

Status of the Null Hypothesis

Researcher's Decision	The null hypothesis is true	The null hypothesis is false
Reject the null hypothesis	Type I Error	Power
Do not reject the null hypothesis	Correct Decision	Type II Error

The Importance of Statistical Power

Statistical power is important because it gives us information about how to successfully conduct research. If we conduct research with too few participants, we can be wasting our own and others' valuable time. In the section that follows, we walk through several examples of caculating statistical power, which will help illuminate its importance. Most important, power gives us an estimate of how many observations to make in order to assess a phenomenon, given an approximate effect size.

Three Factors That Affect Statistical Power

Note that power and its complement, the probability of making a Type II error, may be determined only when the null hypothesis is false. However, because the null hypothesis is believed to be false in each study that includes one or more hypothesis tests, it is important to identify the factors that increase power in order to maximize the likelihood of detecting a false null hypothesis.

1. Power is increased by a higher p level (also known as **alpha**): A study conducted at a p level of 0.05 is more powerful than a study conducted at a p level of 0.01.
2. Power is increased by a one-tailed test: A one-tailed test is more powerful than a two-tailed test.
3. Power is increased by a large sample size: As N increases, power increases.

These points will be illustrated in the following power calculations for a one-tailed z test.

An industrial-organizational psychologist hypothesizes that assembly workers would display a higher level of job satisfaction if they were given a new kind of incentive program. He consults the literature on the effect of incentive programs on job satisfaction and decides that his new program will have a medium effect size. Assessment of the job satisfaction of assembly workers at this company over many years has resulted in a distribution that is approximately normal, with $\mu = 82$ and $\sigma = 7$ on a standard job satisfaction scale. The psychologist plans to provide the new incentive program to 25 randomly selected assembly workers.

    a. What is the power of this study if the null hypothesis is tested at a p level of 0.05?

    b. What is the power of this study if the sample size is increased from 25 to 36 assembly workers?

Step 1. Determine the critical values of z for the given p level (alpha) and a one-tailed test of the null hypothesis. Alpha (α) is 0.05, so the critical value of the z statistic (z_α) is the value that cuts off the upper 5% of the comparison distribution: $z_\alpha = 1.645$. The upper (right) tail of the distribution is the rejection region for the null hypothesis because the psychologist expects that the incentive program will increase job satisfaction among assembly workers. If the researcher conducted a study in which the independent variable was expected to decrease the sample mean score, then the critical value of the z statistic would be -1.645 (again, for a one-tailed test conducted at the 0.05 p level). In the following formulas, σ_M is the standard error (the standard deviation of the comparison distribution of means) and μ_M is the mean of this distribution. Recall that μ_M is always equal to the mean of the population represented by the null hypothesis. Following the notation used in the text, the population represented by the null hypothesis will be designated Population 1, and the population represented by the research hypothesis will be Population 2.

The formula used to compute Cohen's d may be manipulated to determine the mean of Population 2 (μ_2) as follows:

$$\mu_2 = d\sigma + \mu_1 = 0.5(7) + 82 = 3.5 + 82 = 85.5$$

The mean of any distribution of means is always equal to the mean of the parent population, so the mean of Population 2 is the same as the mean of the distribution of means represented by the research hypothesis: $\mu_2 = \mu_{M2}$. Because calculations of power are based on distributions of means, the latter symbol is used. The subscript "2" reminds us that this is the mean of the distribution of all possible means of samples of size N from the population represented by the research hypothesis.

The standard error is computed as follows:

$$\sigma_M = \frac{\sigma}{\sqrt{N}} = \frac{7}{\sqrt{25}} = \frac{7}{5} = 1.4$$

You have the means of the two distributions of means as well as the standard error, so you may sketch the two curves as follows:

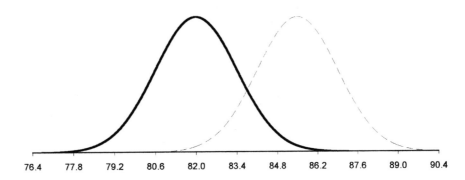

Step 2. Convert the critical value of the z statistic to a sample mean:

$$M_\alpha = z_\alpha \sigma_M + \mu_M = 1.645(1.4) + 82 = 2.303 + 82 = 84.303$$

The area to the right of M_α under the distribution of means represented by the research hypothesis corresponds to power. This area is shaded in the following figure:

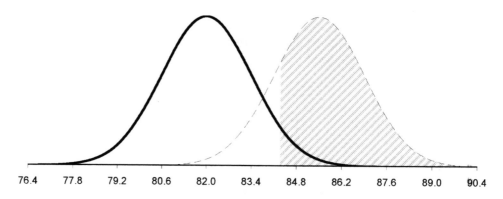

| 76.4 | 77.8 | 79.2 | 80.6 | 82.0 | 83.4 | 84.8 | 86.2 | 87.6 | 89.0 | 90.4 |

Step 3. The remaining step is to look up the shaded area in the previous figure in the table of normal curve percentages in Appendix B in the text. First, we'll have to express the sample mean computed in Step 2 (M_α) as a z statistic. This z statistic is labeled z_{Power} in the following formula.

$$z_{Power} = \frac{M_\alpha - \mu_{M_2}}{\sigma_M} = \frac{84.303 - 85.5}{1.4} = \frac{-1.197}{1.4} = -.855$$

When power is to the right of a negative value of z_{Power}, power is always equal to the area between the mean and z ("%MEAN to z") added to the area to the right of the mean (50%). The power of this study is the sum of the value in the %MEAN to z column for z = 0.86 (30.51%) and the area to the right of the mean (50%), so power = **80.51%**.

To figure power for part b, first determine the new value for the standard error:

$$\sigma_M = \frac{\sigma}{\sqrt{N}} = \frac{7}{\sqrt{36}} = \frac{7}{6} = 1.167$$

Then follow the previous steps:

Step 2. $M_\alpha = z_\alpha \sigma_M + \mu_M = 1.645(1.167) + 82 = 1.92 + 82 = 83.92$

Step 3. $z_{Power} = \dfrac{M_\alpha - \mu_{M_2}}{\sigma_M} = \dfrac{83.92 - 85.5}{1.167} = \dfrac{-1.58}{1.167} = -1.35$

Power = %MEAN to z + 50% = 41.15% + 50% = **91.15%**

As additional exercises, manipulate:
c. the sample size (e.g., try a smaller sample size of 16).
d. alpha (e.g., use 0.01 instead of 0.05).

The solutions are:
c. For $N = 16$, power = 63.87%.
d. For $\alpha = 0.01$, power = 37.07%.

If your answers are different, make sure that you manipulated only the variable identified in the exercise; that is, the sample size should be 16 in both exercises, a medium effect size should be used in parts c and d, and an alpha of 0.05 should be used in part c.

Tables such as those provided by Cohen (1992) are typically used to determine the power of studies that test the null hypothesis. Because sample size is the most easily manipulated of the factors that influence power, researchers typically consult power tables to determine the minimum sample size required to achieve power of 80% (0.8), the level recommended by Cohen and others. Software found on Web sites may also be used to determine the power of a completed study or the sample size needed to achieve a desired level of power. The G*Power program described on page 192 in the text may be downloaded to run from your computer.

STUDY QUESTIONS

1. A sample statistic used to estimate the value of a population parameter is called a(n):
   a. measure of effect size.
   b. confidence limit.
   c. interval estimate.
   d. point estimate.

2. A(n) _____ is a range of values that is likely to include the value of a population parameter.
   a. point estimate
   b. interval estimate
   c. significance test
   d. hypothesis test

3. The phrase "margin of error" is most closely associated with which of the following?
   a. point estimate
   b. interval estimate
   c. confidence interval
   d. effect size

4. A **confidence interval** is centered around the mean of the:
   a. population represented by the research hypothesis.
   b. population represented by the null hypothesis.
   c. comparison distribution.
   d. sample.

5. A researcher constructed a 95% confidence interval from a random sample of 25 scores. Which of the following is the correct interpretation of this confidence interval?
   a. There is a 95% chance that the sample mean is within the confidence interval.
   b. There is a 95% chance that the population mean is within the confidence interval.
   c. There is a 95% chance that the interval does not include the null-hypothesized mean.
   d. The population mean is within 95% of the confidence intervals generated as this one was.

6. A researcher obtains a sample of 25, 90-day-old male rats from the A-1 Animal Breeding Farm and observes the time it takes each one to reach the goal box in a relatively simple maze that she also obtained from the breeding farm. The breeder assures her that the average 90-day-old male A-1 rat runs this maze in 17.6 seconds with a standard deviation of 4.5 seconds. Suppose the researcher computes a mean of 21.4 seconds for her sample of 25 rats. What are the limits of a 95% confidence interval for the true mean running time for the population of A-1 rats?
   a. 15.84 to 19.36
   b. 16.12 to 19.08
   c. 19.92 to 22.88
   d. 19.64 to 23.16

7. The results section of a certain research article reported a 95% confidence interval for the mean to be 0.5583 ± 0.0348. What can you conclude from this result?
   a. The true value of the population mean is 0.5583.
   b. The true value of the population mean is not likely to be 0.5.
   c. The null hypothesis should be rejected because 0.0348 is less than 0.05.
   d. The null hypothesis should not be rejected, because 0.0348 is less than 0.05.

8. If a confidence interval does *not* include the mean specified by the null hypothesis, then the null hypothesis:
   a. may be rejected.
   b. may not be rejected.
   c. is false.
   d. is true.

9. According to the null hypothesis, the number of hours worked in the previous week by college graduates is not different from the mean number of hours worked in the previous week by the population in general (thought to be 40). What decision regarding the validity of the null hypothesis, if any, may be made based on a 95% confidence interval that extends from 46.16 to 49.30 hours as an estimate of the mean number of hours worked the previous week by college graduates?
   a. The null hypothesis is not rejected because the interval does not include the value 40.
   b. The null hypothesis is rejected because the interval does not include the value 40.
   c. The null hypothesis is not rejected because the level of confidence is not < 5%.
   d. There is no way to evaluate the null hypothesis from a confidence interval.

10. A result that is statistically significant is not necessarily an important result. Under which of the following conditions would a significant result be *least* likely to be a result of practical importance?
    a. Effect size and sample size are large.
    b. Effect size and sample size are small.
    c. Effect size is large but sample size is small.
    d. Effect size is small but sample size is large.

11. A standardized measure of effect size discloses the extent to which:
    a. two samples differ in terms of the distance between their respective means.
    b. an increase in sample size is correlated with an increase in the probability of obtaining a statistically significant outcome.
    c. two populations differ in terms of the distance between their respective means.
    d. two populations differ in terms of the variability of the scores around their respective means.

12. As the _____ increases, effect size increases.
    a. size of the sample
    b. population standard deviation
    c. difference between two sample means
    d. difference between two population means

13. How are effect size and sample size related?
    a. negatively: as effect size increases, sample size decreases
    b. positively: as effect size increases, sample size increases
    c. Effect size and sample size are completely unrelated.
    d. The relationship is strong but not linear.

14. Which of the following is the formula for computing effect size?
    a. $\dfrac{M_1 - M_2}{SD}$ b. $\dfrac{\mu_1 - \mu_2}{\dfrac{\sigma}{\sqrt{N}}}$ c. $\dfrac{\mu_{M_1} - \mu_{M_2}}{\dfrac{\sigma}{\sqrt{N}}}$ d. $\dfrac{M_1 - \mu}{\sigma}$

15. You have just computed Cohen's d to be 0.47. This means that:
    a. the means of two distributions of means are 0.47 standard deviations apart.
    b. the means of two populations are 0.47 standard deviations apart.
    c. the ratio of two population standard deviations is 0.47.
    d. there is a 47% chance of rejecting the null hypothesis.

16. Suppose that the Cohen's d statistics computed for two different studies are 0.5 (Study 1) and 1.5 (Study 2). This means that the:
    a. effect sizes of the two studies are comparable if they used the same measure.
    b. effect sizes of the two studies are comparable if they used the same sample size.
    c. effect size for Study 2 is one standard error greater than the effect size for Study 1.
    d. effect size for Study 2 is one standard deviation greater than the effect size for Study 1.

17. Computing the statistic that measures effect size, Cohen's d, is most similar to _____.
    a. converting a raw score to a standard (z) score
    b. computing the population standard deviation
    c. finding an area under the normal curve
    d. computing the population mean

18. For research designed to test a null hypothesis involving two population means, Cohen's effect size conventions are:
    a. small = 0.25; medium = 0.50; large = 0.75
    b. small = 0.30; medium = 0.60; large = 0.90
    c. small = 0.20; medium = 0.50; large = 0.80
    d. Conventions vary depending on other factors.

19. Calculate p_{rep} for a two-tailed z statistics of –0.98.
    a. 0.3270
    b. 16.35
    c. 0.6243
    d. 0.980

20. Calculate p_{rep} for a two-tailed z statistic of 0.55.
    a. 29.12
    b. 0.5824
    c. 0.550
    d. 0.4415

21. The **statistical power** of a study is the probability that the study will:
    a. not have a significant result if the null hypothesis is true.
    b. have a significant result if the research hypothesis is true.
    c. have a significant result if the null hypothesis is true.
    d. not have a significant result if the research hypothesis is true.

22. The traditional minimum requirement for conducting a study is that:
    a. alpha = 0.20.
    b. the effect size is large.
    c. power is greater than alpha.
    d. power is at least 0.80.

23. Based on a number of published studies, the mean self-esteem score in the general population is 50, and the standard deviation is 10 (i.e., $\mu = 50$, $\sigma = 10$). If a researcher predicts that her new program designed to increase a person's self-esteem has a small effect size, then what value would she predict to be the mean of the population of individuals who go through her program of self-esteem improvement?
    a. 48
    b. 55
    c. 60
    d. 52

24. A team of personality psychologists predict that people who experienced a disaster during their childhood will score slightly higher on a measure of fear of disasters (that is, the researchers predict a small positive effect size). It is known from extensive previous testing, using this measure with the population in general, that scores are normally distributed, with a mean of 58 and a standard deviation of 6. The researchers then test their prediction by giving the measure to 120 people who grew up in an area that experienced a devastating forest fire when they were children.

    If the p level is set at 0.05, what is the power of this study?
    a. 0.548
    b. 0.707
    c. − 0.546
    d. 0.546

25. **Alpha** is another name for:
    a. p value.
    b. p level.
    c. power.
    d. effect size.

26. Which of the following would *not* result in an increase in the power of a study?
    a. increase the sample size
    b. use a one-tailed instead of a two-tailed hypothesis test
    c. use a more stringent p level (alpha)
    d. exaggerate the levels of the independent variable

27. At a practical level, researchers are most likely to determine power to help them decide:
    a. how many participants to include in their study.
    b. whether to conduct a one-tailed or a two-tailed test.
    c. whether to set alpha higher or lower than 0.05 (5%).
    d. how large their effect size must be.

28. How is sample size related to power?
    a. It depends on the effect size.
    b. It depends on the standard deviation.
    c. As sample size increases, power increases.
    d. As sample size increases, power decreases.

29. How does sample size affect power?
    a. As sample size increases, the standard deviation of the comparison distribution increases, resulting in less overlap between the two populations.
    b. As sample size increases, the standard deviation of the comparison distribution decreases, resulting in less overlap between the two distributions of means.
    c. As sample size increases, the standard deviation of the comparison distribution increases, resulting in less overlap between the two distributions of means.
    d. As sample size increases, the standard deviation of the comparison distribution decreases, resulting in less overlap between the two populations.

ANSWERS TO CHAPTER 8 STUDY QUESTIONS

Question Number	Correct Answer	Question Number	Correct Answer
1	d, p. 177	16	d, p. 186
2	b, p. 177	17	a, p. 186
3	c, p. 178	18	c, p. 187 (see Table 8-1)
4	d, p. 178	19	c, p. 187
5	b, p. 178	20	d, p. 187
6	d, pp. 178–180	21	b, p. 188
7	b, p. 180	22	d, p. 189
8	a, pp. 180–181	23	d, pp. 187 and 190
9	b, pp. 180–181	24	b, pp. 189–191
10	d, pp. 181–186	25	b, p. 191
11	c, pp. 183–185	26	c, p. 191
12	c, p. 183	27	a, p. 192
13	c, p. 183	28	c, p. 192
14	d, p. 186	29	b, pp. 192–193
15	b, p. 186		

CHAPTER NINE

The Single-Sample *t* Test and the Paired-Samples *t* Test

CHAPTER OUTLINE

The *t* Distributions: Distributions
- Estimating a Population Standard Deviation from the Sample
- Calculating Standard Error for the *t* Statistic
- Using Standard Error to Calculate the *t* Statistic

The Single-Sample *t* Test
- The *t* Table and Degrees of Freedom
- The Six Steps of the Single-Sample *t* Test
- Calculating a Confidence Interval for a Single-Sample *t* Test
- Calculating Effect Size for a Single-Sample *t* Test

The Paired-Samples *t* Test
- Distributions of Mean Differences
- The Six Steps of the Paired-Samples *t* Test
- Calculating a Confidence Interval for a Paired-Samples *t* Test
- Calculating Effect Size for a Paired-Samples *t* Test

LEARNING OBJECTIVES

After studying this chapter, you should be able to:

1. Define each of the following terms and provide examples that are not in the text: *t statistic*; *single-sample t test*; *degrees of freedom*; *paired-samples t test*, and *distributions of mean differences*.

2. Distinguish between the formula used to compute the standard deviation as a descriptive statistic and the slightly adjusted formula used to compute the sample standard deviation as an estimate of the population standard deviation.

3. Explain the concept of *degrees of freedom* in the context of the *t* distributions.

4. Carry out the six steps of hypothesis testing for a single-sample *t* test, and a paired-samples *t* test.

5. Compute confidence intervals and effect size for a single-sample *t* test and a paired-samples *t* test.

CHAPTER REVIEW

In this chapter, you will learn about the *t* distribution and the *t* tests available. In total, you will learn about three *t* tests: one that compares a sample to a population (the single-sample *t* test), one that compares two samples that contain the same or matched people in a within-groups design (the paired-samples *t* test), and one that compares two different samples in a between-groups design (the independent samples *t* test).

Each of the three *t* tests will be illustrated using the issue of weight gained over the winter holiday season. A single-sample *t* test might compare weight gained by college students compared to weight gained in the nation overall (when the mean of the population is known but the standard deviation is unknown). A paired-samples *t* test could be used to compare weight gained by 20 women over the winter holiday during their first year of college to the same measurement taken during their third year of college. An independent samples *t* test could be used to compare weight gained by groups of female versus male college students during their first winter break.

In this chapter we focus on the single-sample and paired-samples *t* tests. You will learn about independent samples *t* tests in Chapter 10.

> The *t* Distributions

In all cases, *t* tests are used when we know the mean but do not know the standard deviation of the population. They are also used when we are comparing two groups to each other. There are many different *t* distributions, because the shape of the distribution changes as a function of sample size. As sample size increases, the *t* distribution approximates the *z* distribution.

Estimating Population Standard Deviation from the Sample

When the population standard deviation (*σ*) is not known (a common situation), it must be *estimated* from the sample standard deviation. However, the formula used to compute the standard deviation as a descriptive statistic (*SD*, left, in the following equations) consistently *underestimates* the value of the population standard deviation; you inherently don't measure the full range of scores in a population when assessing just one sample. An adjustment to the formula (*s*, right, in the following equations) makes the sample standard deviation a better estimate of *σ*.

$$SD = \sqrt{\frac{\Sigma(X-M)^2}{N}} \qquad s = \sqrt{\frac{\Sigma(X-M)^2}{N-1}}$$

As you can see in the equations, the only change in the computation occurs in the denominator, changing from N to $N - 1$. By reducing the size of the denominator, we increase the value for s. This helps to address the concern that a standard deviation calculated on a sample may underestimate the population variability.

The calculation of s follows the same steps as the calculation of SD. See pages 204–205 in the text for an example.

Calculating Standard Error for the t Statistic

Just as with the z statistic, the standard deviation for scores needs to be translated into a measure of variability of means, or a measure of standard error. This computation is done in the same way as the computation for the z test (shown on the left here), but we use s because σ is unknown (shown on the right).

$$\sigma_M = \frac{\sigma}{\sqrt{N}} \qquad\qquad s_M = \frac{s}{\sqrt{N}}$$

In both cases, the standard error of the distribution of means is smaller than the standard deviation of the population of scores. Be careful when computing s and s_M that you divide by $N - 1$ in the first computation and $\sqrt{N}$ in the second computation.

Using Standard Error to Calculate the t Statistic

The formula for the single-sample t statistic is presented in this section. This formula is identical to the formula for the z statistic except that the standard error is based on an estimate rather than information known about a population. Specifically, this t statistic tells us how far away a sample mean is from a population mean in terms of estimated standard errors.

$$t = \frac{(M - \mu_M)}{s_M}$$

Remember that the change from σ_M to s_M results in a slightly larger denominator. A larger denominator results in a smaller test statistic, so t statistics tend to be smaller or less extreme than z statistics. Another way to think about this is that when we estimate things, when we know we are approximating something, we err on the side of being conservative in our conclusions.

> The Single-Sample *t* Test

Testing the null hypothesis with a **single-sample *t* test** is very similar to hypothesis testing with the single sample z test that you learned in the previous chapter. The difference in these tests is found in the denominator, whereas with the z test we know the population standard error, we do not know this with the t test.

$$z = \frac{(M - \mu_M)}{\sigma / \sqrt{N}} \qquad t = \frac{(M - \mu_M)}{s / \sqrt{N}}$$

The t *Table and Degrees of Freedom*

There are many different t distributions and they vary by **degrees of freedom** (*df*). Degrees of freedom are the number of scores or observations that are "free to vary" when we compute an estimate of the population. The critical cutoff for a t test changes with degrees of freedom because the distribution changes shape. Specifically, as degrees of freedom increase, the critical cutoff for t moves toward the center of the distribution (less extreme) because the tails of the distribution flatten out.

As you can see in the following figure, t distributions look very much like normal distributions but with a flatter center and fatter tails. Again, as the size of the sample increases (and *df* increases), the sample standard deviation becomes a more stable estimate of the population standard deviation, and the t distribution looks progressively more like the normal distribution.

We will compute degrees of freedom and determine critical cutoffs for an example problem in the next section.

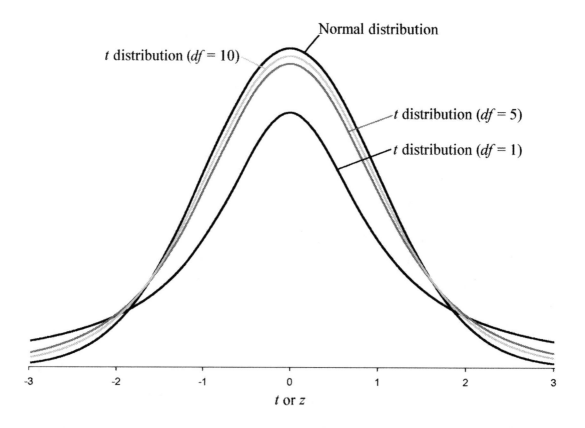

The Six Steps of the Single-Sample t Test

Let's illustrate the six steps of hypothesis testing using the single-sample t test with an example problem.

A school psychologist believes that the one of the elementary schools in her school district consistently produces students with superior reading scores. Accordingly, she randomly selected the following 15 Reading Achievement Test Scores from the files of first-grade children at this elementary school. The national norm (that is, μ) on this test is 200. Use the 0.05 p level to test the null hypothesis that the scores recorded for the children who attend this elementary school are from a population in which the mean Reading Achievement Test score is 200.

X	$X - M$	$(X - M)^2$		
177	−30.8	948.64	$M - \mu_M =$	7.8
222	14.2	201.64		
189	−18.8	353.44	$s =$	15.87
206	−1.8	3.24	$s_M =$	4.10
196	−11.8	139.24		
195	−12.8	163.84	$t =$	1.90
221	13.2	174.24	$t_{critical} =$	2.145
205	−2.8	7.84		
222	14.2	201.64		
195	−12.8	163.84		
231	23.2	538.24		
204	−3.8	14.44		
232	24.2	585.64		
213	5.2	27.04		
209	1.2	1.44		

$\Sigma =$ 3117 $SS =$ 3524.4
$N =$ 15 $s^2 =$ 251.74
$M =$ 207.8

Step 1. Identify the populations, distribution, and assumptions.

- The two populations being compared are first-grade students at the elementary school in her district and first-grade students in the nation.
- The comparison distribution is one of sample means, and we are conducting a single-sample *t* test because we know the mean of the population but not the standard deviation.
- The data meet two assumptions of the test: the dependent variable is a scale variable and the data were randomly selected. However, we do not know how the population data are distributed and we have fewer than 30 observations, so we should proceed with some caution.

Step 2. State the null and research hypotheses.

Null Hypothesis: First-grade students at this school are no different than the nation in reading achievement. $H_0: \mu_1 = \mu_2 = 200$

Research Hypothesis: First-grade students at this school perform different from the nation. $H_1: \mu_1 \neq \mu_2 \neq 200$

Step 3. Determine the characteristics of the comparison distribution: These values are shown with the data above.

Step 4. Determine the critical values, or cutoffs.

$$df = N - 1 = 15 - 1 = 14$$

For a two-tailed test with 14 *df* and a *p* level of 0.05, the critical cutoffs are –2.145 and 2.145.

Step 5. Calculate the test statistic.

$$t = \frac{(M - \mu_M)}{s_M} = \frac{207.8 - 200}{4.10} = 1.90$$

Step 6. Make a Decision: The null hypothesis should not be rejected because the computed value of the *t* statistic (1.90) is not more extreme than the critical value of *t* (2.145) for a two-tailed test with 14 degrees of freedom conducted at the 0.05 *p* level.

This statistic might be reported in a sentence like the following example:

$M = 207.8$, $SD = 15.87$) failed to reach significance, $t(14) = 1.90$, $p > 0.05$

Calculating a Confidence Interval for a Single-Sample t Test

We calculate the confidence interval around the sample mean for the group of 15 first-graders, $M = 207.8$.

Steps 1 and 2. We start by drawing a normal curve centered on 207.8 with the 95% confidence interval noted. We place 2.5% in each tail for a total of 5%.

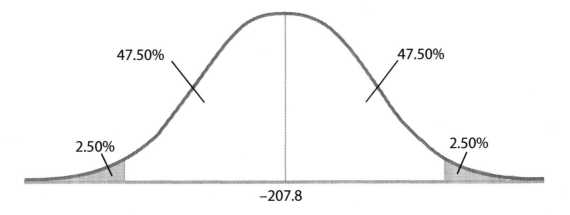

47.50%   47.50%

2.50%   2.50%

−207.8

Step 3. Look up the *t* statistic that creates the 2.5% cutoff regions in each tail. For this statistical analysis, we look up the *t* statistic for a two-tailed test with 14 *df* at a *p* level of 0.05. The critical cutoffs are −2.145 and 2.145.

Step 4. The critical cutoffs for *t* now are converted into raw score values using the following equations.

$$M_{lower} = -t(s_M) + M_{sample} = -2.145(4.10) + 207.8 = 199.01$$

$$M_{upper} = t(s_M) + M_{sample} = 2.145(4.10) + 207.8 = 216.59$$

Step 5. To check our work, we verify that the sample mean, 207.8, falls directly in the center of the confidence interval.

$$199.01 - 207.8 = -8.79 \qquad\qquad 216.59 - 207.8 = 8.79$$

Our calculations are accurate. Because the population mean of 200 falls within the confidence interval, we confirm our decision to fail to reject the null hypothesis.

Calculating Effect Size for a Single-Sample t Test

The effect size calculation here is similar to that for the z statistic.

$$\text{Cohen's } d = \frac{M - \mu}{s} = \frac{207.8 - 200}{15.87} = 0.49$$

This is a medium effect size and can be reported with the test statistic, as shown:

> The comparison of these first-grade students to the nation on reading test scores ($M = 207.8$, $SD = 15.87$) failed to reach significance, $t(14) = 1.90$, $p > 0.05$, $d = 0.49$.

> The Paired-Samples *t* Test

When there are two samples of scores to be compared, the choice is between the paired samples t test and the independent samples t test. This choice, in turn, depends on the experimental design. The **paired-samples *t* test** is used to analyze the data when the data are from *within-groups designs*, whereas the independent samples t test is used when the data are from *between-groups designs*. You may recall from Chapter 1 that a between-groups design includes two or more independent groups—that is, the individuals assigned to each group are unrelated to each other and to the individuals assigned to the other group(s). In contrast, the samples of scores analyzed for a within-groups design are *correlated*. The most commonly used within-groups design is a repeated-measures design. In this design, the same participants serve in all conditions of the study, so the correlation between the scores obtained from the same participants in different conditions is not surprising. The simplest form of a repeated measures design is called the *before-after* (or pretest-posttest) *design*. In this design, scores from a sample of participants are obtained before and after some treatment or intervention. Another type of within-groups design is called a matched-pairs (or matched-groups) design. Matched groups designs include samples of participants who are related in some way, either because they are from the same family (e.g., husbands and wives, brothers and sisters) or because the otherwise unrelated members of each pair of participants were matched on some variable related to the dependent variable before they were randomly assigned to the different conditions of the study.

So, a paired-samples t test should be used to analyze the data from a within-groups design because this test acknowledges the correlation, or dependency, between the scores obtained from the same group of participants who are measured under each condition of the study (repeated measures designs) or from different groups of participants who are either related in some way or matched on some variable (matched groups designs). A repeated measures design is more likely to detect the effect of an independent variable if there is one, because scores obtained from the same individuals are less variable than scores obtained from independent groups of participants. Thus, for a given treatment effect, the denominator of the paired-samples t statistic will be smaller than the denominator of an independent-samples t statistic, and the value of the paired-sample t statistic will be larger as a result. Larger t statistics have smaller p values and thus are more likely to meet the criterion of statistical significance, in other words, they have more power.

Distributions of Mean Differences

Raw scores and z scores are compared to distributions of scores, z and single-sample t statistics are compared to distributions of means, and paired-samples t statistics are compared to distributions of mean differences. As illustrated in the text, these hypothetical distributions of mean differences are created by sampling a certain number of paired scores, computing the change for each person (a difference score), and averaging these values (a mean difference). This computation would be done repeatedly for samples of the same size. These mean differences are then plotted to create a distribution of mean differences. For paired-samples t tests we are comparing paired or matched observations, and this is done by computing differences and averaging them.

The Six Steps of the Paired-Samples t Test

As described, the first step in conducting a paired-samples t test is to record two data points for each person/thing being observed or for pairs in a match. The scores are then compared by computing difference scores. Positive difference scores typically reflect an increase in the variable being measured while negative differences reflect a decrease.

We will work through the six steps of hypothesis testing with an example problem:

An educational psychologist designed a program to provide intensive training in the improvement of SAT scores for high school athletes who were recruited to play for NCAA Division I university football teams but did not qualify because of low SAT scores. A pilot test of the program was administered to athletes between the October and May SAT testing dates. Use the 0.05 p level to test the null hypothesis that the program has no effect on the SAT scores of high school football players like those participating in this study.

Step 1. Identify the populations, comparison distribution, and assumptions.

Both populations consist of the SAT scores of elite high school football players with Division I scholarships pending improvement of their SAT scores. Population 1 is the population of scores following the intensive training program and Population 2 is the population of scores prior to the intensive training program. The comparison distribution is the distribution of all possible mean difference scores obtained by subtracting the before scores from the after scores. SAT scores are assumed to be measured on an interval scale. The population distributions have not been well-studied, but are thought to be approximately normal or at least do not depart from normality enough to compromise the robustness of the paired-samples *t* test that will be used to analyze the sample of difference scores. The participants in the sample are volunteers, so the generalization of these results is limited to populations composed of individuals who are similar to the participants studied in this sample.

Step 2. State the null and research hypotheses.

The null hypothesis is that the mean of the population of after scores (Population 1) is equal to the mean of the population of before scores (Population 2). The research (alternative) hypothesis is that the mean of the population of after scores is not equal to the mean of the population of before scores. In symbols,

$$H_0: \mu_1 = \mu_2$$
$$H_1: \mu_1 \neq \mu_2$$

Step 3. Determine the characteristics of the comparison distribution.

The comparison distribution is the distribution of all possible mean difference scores for samples of $N = 8$ that might be obtained under the assumption that the null hypothesis is true. According to the null hypothesis, the mean of this distribution of difference scores must be 0, because the treatment (the intensive training program) is ineffective (*nullus = not any* effect); $\mu_M = 0$ and s_M is shown below.

Step 4. Determine the critical, or cutoff, values of the test statistic.

It is a *t* statistic from the distribution defined by $N - 1 = 8 - 1 = 7$ degrees of freedom. This is a two-tailed test conducted at the 0.05 *p* level, so there are two critical values of this *t* statistic: the negative value cuts off the lower 2.5% of the comparison distribution, and the positive value cuts off the upper 2.5% of the comparison distribution. From Table B.2 in the apprendix of the text, these values are –2.365 and 2.365.

Step 5. Calculate the test statistic.

SAT (before)	Treatment	SAT (after)	Difference	Diff - M_{diff}	Squared deviation
600		610	10	−10.625	112.891
610		600	−10	−30.625	937.891
640		690	50	29.375	862.891
720		750	30	9.375	87.891
710		710	0	−20.625	425.391
680		715	35	14.375	206.641
690		700	10	−10.625	112.891
740		780	40	19.375	375.391

$$\sum = 165$$
$$N = 8$$
$$M_{diff} = \sum / N = 20.625$$

$$SS = 3121.878$$
$$s^2 = 445.983$$
$$s = 21.118$$
$$s_M = 7.466$$
$$t = 2.763$$
$$t_{critical} = 2.365$$

Step 6. Make a decision.

The null hypothesis may be rejected, because the computed value of the *t* statistic (2.763) is more extreme than the critical value (2.635). The educational psychologist's intensive training program is apparently effective in altering the SAT scores of elite high school football players like those who volunteered to participate in this study. However, this was a pilot program conducted with a small sample of athletes from one region of the country. Before even tentatively considering the program to be a success, the educational psychologist will replicate this study with a larger, more diverse, sample of athletes and will work to achieve a level of program effectiveness that enables student-athletes with subqualifying SAT scores to achieve qualifying scores. Reported formally, this would be expressed as $t(7) - 2.763$, $p < 0.05$.

Calculating a Confidence Interval for a Paired-Samples t Test

We calculate the confidence interval around the sample mean difference for the group of 8 football players, $M = 20.625$.

Steps 1 and 2. We start by drawing a normal curve, centered on 20.625, with the 95% confidence interval noted. We place 2.5% in each tail for a total of 5%.

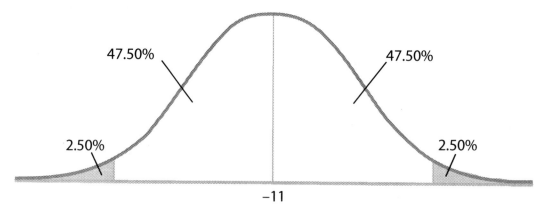

47.50%   47.50%

2.50%   2.50%

−11

Step 3. Look up the *t* statistic that creates the 2.5% cutoff regions in each tail. For this statistical analysis, we look up the *t* statistic for a two-tailed test with 7 *df* at a *p* level of 0.05. The critical cutoffs are −2.365 and 2.365.

Step 4. The critical cutoffs for *t* now are converted into raw score values using the following equations.

$$M_{lower} = -t(s_M) + M_{sample} = -2.365(7.466) + 20.625 = 2.968$$

$$M_{upper} = t(s_M) + M_{sample} = 2.365(7.466) + 20.625 = 38.282$$

Our 95% confidence interval is [2.968, 38.282]. We can be confident that mean differences calculated on similar samples of size 8 will fall within these cutoffs 95% of the time.

Step 5. To check our work, we verify that the sample mean, 20.625, falls directly in the center of the confidence interval.

$$20.625 - 2.968 = 17.657 \qquad 20.625 - 38.282 = -17.657$$

Our calculations are accurate. Because the null hypothesized mean difference of zero does not fall within the confidence interval, we confirm our decision to reject the null hypothesis.

Calculating Effect Size for a Paired-Samples t Test

The effect size calculation here is similar to that for the *z* statistic:

$$\text{Cohen's } d = \frac{M - \mu}{s} = \frac{20.625 - 0}{21.118} = 0.977$$

This calculation tells us that our sample mean difference (20.625) and hypothesized population mean difference (0) are 0.977 standard deviations apart. This effect size is large and can be reported with the test statistic, as shown:

The SAT training resulted in a significant shift in SAT scores, $t(7) = 2.763$, $p < 0.05$, $d = 0.977$.

STUDY QUESTIONS

1. How is a single-sample *t* test different from a *z* test?
   a. The comparison distribution for the *t* test is not a normal curve.
   b. Using the *z* test requires having to estimate the population standard deviation.
   c. Using the *t* test requires having to estimate the population mean.
   d. The *t* test is more likely to produce a statistically significant result.

2. The shape of a *t* distribution differs most from the shape of the normal curve when the:
   a. sample size is large.
   b. sample size is small.
   c. population is large.
   d. population is small.

3. Consider the following formula:

$$\sqrt{\frac{\sum (M-X)^2}{(N-1)}}$$

What does this formula compute?
   a. the standard deviation
   b. a corrected estimate of the sample standard deviation
   c. an uncorrected estimate of the population standard deviation
   d. a corrected estimate of the population standard deviation

4. The formula used to compute a sample standard deviation was introduced in Chapter 2. However, the standard deviation computed using this formula is not a very accurate estimate of the population standard deviation. Consequently, statisticians adjusted the formula to improve the accuracy of the sample standard deviation as an estimate of the population standard deviation. Which of the following statements is *most* accurate regarding this adjustment?
   a. The size of the adjustment varies with sample size: as the size of the sample increases, the size of the adjustment increases.
   b. The size of the adjustment varies with sample size: as the size of the sample increases, the size of the adjustment decreases.
   c. The size of the adjustment varies with population size: as the size of the population increases, the size of the adjustment increases.
   d. The size of the adjustment varies with population size: as the size of the population increases, the size of the adjustment decreases.

5. The shape of *t* distributions vary according to the:
   a. number of participants in the sample used to estimate the population standard deviation.
   b. standard deviation of the population from which the sample was taken.
   c. mean of the population from which the sample was taken.
   d. mean of the sample.

6. Which of the following formulas is used to compute an estimate of the standard error?

   a. $\dfrac{s}{\sqrt{N}}$ b. $\dfrac{s}{\sqrt{N-1}}$ c. $\dfrac{\sigma}{\sqrt{N}}$ d. $\dfrac{\sigma}{\sqrt{N-1}}$

7. The symbol s_M represents an estimate of the standard deviation of the:
   a. population specified by the research hypothesis.
   b. population specified by the null hypothesis.
   c. comparison distribution of means.
   d. scores in the sample.

8. The *t* statistic computed for a single-sample *t* test is a measure of the distance between:
   a. a sample mean and a population mean in terms of the standard deviation.
   b. a sample mean and a population mean in terms of the standard error.
   c. two population means in terms of the population standard deviation.
   d. two population means in terms of the standard error.

9. To use a single-sample *t* test to decide whether a sample comes from a population with a specific mean, all of the following *except* the _____ must be known.
   a. sample mean
   b. population mean
   c. sample standard deviation
   d. population standard deviation

10. A single-sample *t* test is used:
    a. when the population standard deviation is known.
    b. to determine whether a sample is from a population with a known mean.
    c. to determine whether the means of unrelated samples are significantly different.
    d. to determine whether participants' scores change from one condition to another.

11. With respect to the family of *t* distributions, what is the relationship between sample size (*N*) and degrees of freedom (*df*)?
    a. as *N* increases, *df* increases
    b. as *N* increases, *df* decreases
    c. The relationship depends on the sample size.
    d. *N* and *df* are not related.

12. A researcher studying the effects of exercise on depression assesses depression levels for 30 people participating in an intense 6-week exercise program and compares the group average to that known for the population. What are the degrees of freedom for this study?
    a. 29
    b. 30
    c. 59
    d. 60

13. For any particular degrees of freedom, there is (are):
    a. an infinite number of *t* distributions, each determined by the population standard deviation.
    b. an infinite number of *t* distributions, each determined by the population mean.
    c. two *t* distributions, one for one-tailed tests and one for two-tailed tests.
    d. only one *t* distribution.

14. Because critical values are _____ extreme for a two-tailed test than for a one-tailed test, it is _____ likely that a two-tailed test will yield a significant result.
    a. less; more
    b. less; less
    c. more; less
    d. more; more

15. Excerpt from a *t* Table:

df	One-Tailed Tests			Two-Tailed Tests		
	0.10	0.05	0.01	0.10	0.05	0.01
18	1.330	1.734	2.552	1.734	2.101	2.878
19	1.328	1.729	2.539	1.729	2.093	2.861
20	1.325	1.725	2.528	1.725	2.086	2.845
21	1.323	1.721	2.518	1.721	2.080	2.831
22	1.321	1.717	2.508	1.717	2.074	2.819

A certain fifth-grade teacher believes, rather strongly, that her classes are always better prepared than those of her teaching colleagues for the Standards of Learning (SOL) tests given near the end of each academic year. This year, her class of 20 students earned a mean score of 107 with a standard deviation of 14. The teacher decides to conduct a *t* test using a *p* level of 0.01. What is the critical value of *t* for this proposed analysis?
    a. 1.325
    b. 1.725
    c. 2.540
    d. 2.861

16. A counseling psychologist hypothesized that having clients sign an agreement to attend a minimum number of counseling sessions increases the number of sessions attended. Suppose that the number of sessions attended at a certain university counseling center is approximately normally distributed with a mean (μ) of 4.6 and an unknown standard deviation (σ). Five students sign an agreement to attend at least 10 sessions. The number of sessions actually attended by these 5 students is as follows: 6, 4, 4, 14, and 12. The psychologist used the following formulas to analyze the data. Which one of the formulas is incorrect?

   a. $M = \dfrac{\sum X}{N}$ b. $s = \sqrt{\dfrac{\sum(X-M)^2}{(N-1)}}$ c. $S_M = \dfrac{s}{\sqrt{N-1}}$ d. $t = \dfrac{M - \mu_M}{S_M}$

17. Refer to the previous question. The counseling psychologist prepared a manuscript for publication in a journal that requires all submitted manuscripts to be formatted according to the editorial guidelines of the American Psychological Association (APA). Which of the following sentences is formatted according to APA guidelines?
    a. Clients who signed an agreement to attend at least 10 sessions (M = 8.00, SD = 4.69) did not attend more sessions than clients who did not sign such an agreement, t(4) = 1.62, p > 0.05.
    b. Clients who signed an agreement to attend at least 10 sessions (*M* = 8.00, *SD* = 4.69) did not attend more sessions than clients who did not sign such an agreement, t(4) = 1.62, p > 0.05.
    c. Clients who signed an agreement to attend at least 10 sessions (M = 8.00, SD = 4.69) did not attend more sessions than clients who did not sign such an agreement, *t*(4) = 1.62, *p* > 0.05.
    d. Clients who signed an agreement to attend at least 10 sessions (*M* = 8.00, *SD* = 4.69) did not attend more sessions than clients who did not sign such an agreement, *t*(4) = 1.62, *p* > 0.05.

18. Imagine that the mean depression score for the population is known to be 120. Data collected on 30 depressed people following participation in an exercise program result in a mean depression score of 118, with a standard deviation of 4 (calculated as *s*). What is the *t* statistic?
    a. 2.045
    b. –2.045
    c. –2.739
    d. 29

19. Which of the following is the correct 95% confidence interval for the problem described in problem 18?
    a. [114, 122]
    b. [116.51, 119.49]
    c. [114.5, 121.5]
    d. [110.7, 125.3]

20. Compute the effect size for the problem described in problem 18.
    a. 2.739
    b. 0.50
    c. –2.739
    d. –0.50

21. A research design in which each participant serves in both conditions of the study (e.g., in both the experimental condition and the control condition) is called a(n) _____ design.
    a. between-groups
    b. within-groups
    c. mixed
    d. independent-samples

22. The paired-samples (or dependent-samples) *t* test is almost exactly the same as the single-sample *t* test. The "difference" is that, whereas the individual raw scores from a single sample are analyzed by the single-sample *t* test, the paired-samples *t* test analyzes a single sample of _____ scores.
    a. *t*
    b. mean
    c. difference
    d. *z*

23. A nondirectional null hypothesis tested with a paired-samples *t* test is that the mean of:
    a. Population 1 is greater than or equal to the mean of Population 2.
    b. Population 1 is less than or equal to the mean of Population 2.
    c. the population of difference scores is not equal to zero.
    d. the population of difference scores is equal to zero.

24. Conducting a(n) _____ requires two scores for each participant.
    a. single-sample *t* test
    b. paired-samples *t* test
    c. independent-samples *t* test
    d. *z* test

25. Beck, Steer, and Brown (1996) compared scores on the Beck Depression Inventory-II (BDI-II) administered to a sample of 26 outpatients at two therapy sessions one week apart and reported no significance difference between the mean total scores. Which of the following analyses was used to compare the two mean scores on the BDI-II?
    a. *z* test
    b. single-sample *t* test
    c. paired-samples *t* test
    d. independent-samples *t* test

26. A researcher studying the effects of exercise on depression assesses depression levels for 30 people before and after a 6-week exercise program, for a total of 60 measurements. What are the degrees of freedom for this study?
    a. 29
    b. 30
    c. 59
    d. 60

27. Depression scores for 4 people before and after a 6-week exercise program follow. Compute a paired samples t test for these data.

Before	After
117	118
126	122
130	115
141	133

    a. −6.5
    b. 6.758
    c. 3.379
    d. −1.924

28. Which of the following is the correct 95% confidence interval for problem 27?
    a. [−17.252, 4.252]
    b. [−10.4, 2.79]
    c. [2.516, 16.412]
    d. [−8.182, −1.119]

29. Compute the effect size for problem 27.
    a. 0.675
    b. −0.962
    c. −1.924
    d. 3.182

ANSWERS TO CHAPTER 9 STUDY QUESTIONS

Question Number	Correct Answer	Question Number	Correct Answer
1	a, p. 203	17	d, p. 212 (Symbols for descriptive statistics, test statistics, and probability values must be italicized.)
2	b, p. 203		
3	d, pp. 203–204		
4	b, pp. 203–205	18	c, pp. 296 and 211–212
5	a, pp. 203 and 208	19	b, p. 214
6	a, p. 205	20	d, p. 214
7	c, p. 205	21	b, p. 216
8	b, p. 206	22	c, p. 216
9	d, pp. 206 and 211–212	23	d, p. 217
10	b, p. 207	24	b, pp. 216, 218
11	a, p. 208	25	c, pp. 216–218
12	a, p. 208	26	a, p. 219
13	d, pp. 208–209	27	d, pp. 218–219
14	c, pp. 208–210	28	a, p. 220
15	c, pp. 208–210	29	b, p. 221
16	c, pp. 204–206 and 211–212		

CHAPTER TEN

The Independent-Samples *t* Test

CHAPTER OUTLINE

Conducting an Independent-Samples *t* Test
- A Distribution of Differences Between Means
- The Six Steps of an Independent-Samples *t* Test
- Reporting the Statistics

Beyond Hypothesis Testing
- Confidence Interval
- Effect Size

LEARNING OBJECTIVES

After studying this chapter, you should be able to:

1. Define each of the following terms and provide examples that are not in the text: *independent-samples* t *test*; *distribution of differences between means*; *pooled variance*; and *weighted average*.
2. Carry out the six steps of hypothesis testing for an independent-samples *t* test.
3. Compute a confidence interval and effect size for an independent-samples *t* test.

CHAPTER REVIEW

> Conducting an Independent-Samples *t* Test

In this chapter, we learn about a new comparison distribution and the *t* test that compares two different samples in a between-groups design, the **independent-samples *t* test**.

Remember that in a between-groups design, participants experience only one level of the independent variable. This type of design is commonly used because treatments must be uniquely administered, that is, participants cannot experience more than one condition. For example, if we compare two brands of car windshields to see which one resists chips better, we would need to install those windshields on different cars; it would not be physically possible to install them on the same car at the same time. In the social sciences, any comparison between different groups, like men and women or different ethnic or religious groups, involves the comparison of independent samples. In medical research, it is often not possible to treat a patient with more than one therapy, so we compare different groups of people each receiving one treatment. The *t* test used to make these comparisons, the independent-samples *t* test, is logically identical to the *t* tests you learned about in Chapter 9.

A Distribution of Differences Between Means

When we assess and compare two groups that are unmatched or independent, we compare the means of those two groups. Let's consider how the paired-samples and the independent-samples *t* tests are different from each other.

When conducting a paired-samples *t* test, we compare scores by computing differences for each matched pair and then take an average of the difference scores. If we wanted to compare the job satisfaction of people before the economic crash of 2008 with their satisfaction after many of their colleagues and friends lost their jobs, we would get two measurements from each participant, compute a difference between each pair of scores, and then take an average of all the differences. The comparison distribution for the paired-samples *t* test contains mean differences.

With the independent-samples *t* test, we simply compute an average for a group and compare the group average with the average from a separate or independent group. If we wanted to compare the job satisfaction of men and women, we would compute an average satisfaction for men and an average satisfaction for women and then compare the averages; we would look at the differences between the two means. The comparison distribution for the independent-samples *t* test contains differences between means.

The Six Steps of an Independent-Samples t *Test*

Before progressing systematically through the steps, let's work through a problem while focusing on the logic and the mathematics behind the test. Consider this first problem, which compares two groups, an experimental group and a control group of different sizes. Note that Population 1 and Population 2 can also be called Population *x* and Population *y*.

Population 1 is the distribution of scores represented by the research hypothesis. This distribution consists of the scores recorded for individuals who experience the treatment.

Population 2 is the distribution of scores represented by the null hypothesis. This distribution consists of the scores recorded for individuals who do not experience the treatment.

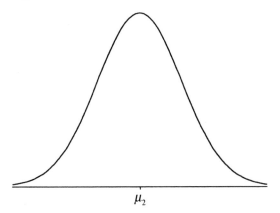

μ_1

μ_2

If the null hypothesis is correct, then the scores recorded for individuals receiving the experimental treatment have the same mean and variance as the scores recorded for individuals who do not receive the experimental treatment—that is, $\mu_1 = \mu_2$.

The following figures represent the distributions of means of samples of size N from each of these populations. Each distribution of means has the same mean as its parent population:

$$\mu_1 = \mu_{M_1} \text{ and } \mu_2 = \mu_{M_2}$$

And a variance equal to the common population variance divided by the sample size:

Distribution of means from Population 1(x)

$$\sigma^2_M = \frac{\sigma^2}{N}$$

Distribution of means from Population 2(y)

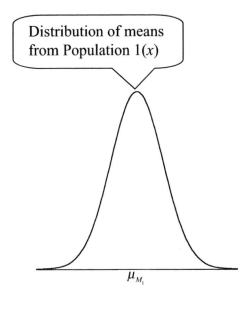

μ_{M_1}

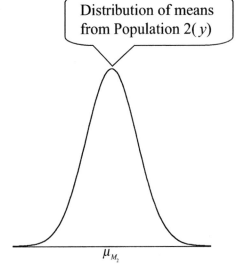

μ_{M_2}

The appropriate comparison distribution is constructed by randomly selecting one mean at a time from each distribution of means, and subtracting one from the other. The result is a distribution of all possible differences between means of samples of size N from each distribution of means.

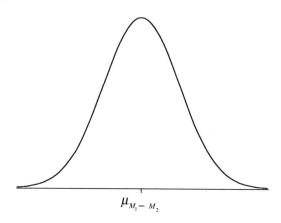

$$\mu_{M_1 - M_2}$$

This comparison distribution of differences between means has a mean of zero and a variance equal to the sum of the variances of each distribution of means:

$$\sigma^2_{difference} = \sigma^2_{M_1} + \sigma^2_{M_2}$$

However, the population variance (assumed to be the same for both populations) is not known, so it must be estimated from the variances of both samples. Thus, s_1^2 and s_2^2 are used to estimate σ^2 (the common population variance). Because the sample variances are not likely to be the same value, they are averaged to produce the best estimate of the population variance. This average must take into account the possibility that the two samples are equal in size, that is, there is no requirement that $N_1 = N_2$. Therefore, the formula for estimating the value of the population variance covers both possibilities: when $N_1 = N_2$ and when $N_1 \neq N_2$. This formula computes a weighted average called s^2_{pooled}. This idea is developed with the following worked examples. The goal is to compute an estimate of the variance of the comparison distribution of differences between means ($\sigma^2_{difference}$). This estimate is $s^2_{difference}$.

The comparison distribution of differences between means may be converted to a t distribution, using the formula:

$$t = \frac{M_1 - M_2}{s_{difference}}$$

This results in a t distribution with degrees of freedom based on both samples: $df_{total} = df_1 + df_2 = N_1 + N_2 - 2$.

Use the group statistics in the following table to test the null hypothesis that $\mu_1 = \mu_2$.

	N	df	M	s^2
Experimental Group	21	20	95	60
Control Group	31	30	90	80

The first step is to compute an estimate the population variance, which is assumed to be the same for Population 1 (the population from which the experimental group is selected) and Population 2 (the population from which the control group is selected). A weighted average of the two variances must be computed to reflect the relative contributions of the different sample sizes, expressed as degrees of freedom. The weighted average of the two sample variances is the pooled estimate of the population variance (s^2_{pooled}):

$$s^2_{pooled} = \frac{df_1}{df_{total}} s_1^2 + \frac{df_2}{df_{total}} s_2^2 = \frac{20}{50}(60) + \frac{30}{50}(80) = (.4)(60) + (.6)(80) = 24 + 48 = 72$$

The next step is to compute the variance of each distribution of means ($s^2_{M_1}$ and $s^2_{M_2}$). The pooled estimate of the population variance (72) is divided by the respective sample sizes (*not* the degrees of freedom) to produce the following values:

$$s^2_{M_1} = \frac{s^2_{pooled}}{N_1} = \frac{72}{21} = 3.429 \qquad s^2_{M_2} = \frac{s^2_{pooled}}{N_2} = \frac{72}{31} = 2.323$$

The variances of the two distributions of means are summed to produce an estimate of the variance of the distribution of differences between means:

$$s^2_{difference} = s^2_{M_1} + s^2_{M_2} = 3.429 + 2.323 = 5.752$$

The standard deviation of the distribution of differences between means is computed as the square root of the variance of the distribution of differences between means.

$$s_{difference} = \sqrt{s^2_{difference}} = \sqrt{5.752} = 2.398$$

The *t* statistic may now be computed as follows:

$$t = \frac{M_1 - M_2}{S_{\text{difference}}} = \frac{95 - 90}{2.398} = \frac{5}{2.398} = 2.09$$

The computed value of the *t* statistic (2.09) is compared to the *t* distribution for 20 + 30 = 50 degrees of freedom. Table B.2 in the appendix of the text does not include entries for 50 degrees of freedom, so the conservative choice is to use the critical value of *t* for 40 degrees of freedom, because this is the table value that is closest to, but less than, 50. The critical value of *t* for a two-tailed test conducted at a *p* level of 0.05 and 40 degrees of freedom is 2.021. The computed value of the *t* statistic is more extreme than the critical value, so the null hypothesis may be rejected. It may be concluded that the samples means are significantly different. The following figure is the comparison distribution of the *t* statistic, showing the two-tailed critical region for a *p* level of 0.05 and the shaded region corresponding to the *p* value of the computed statistic.

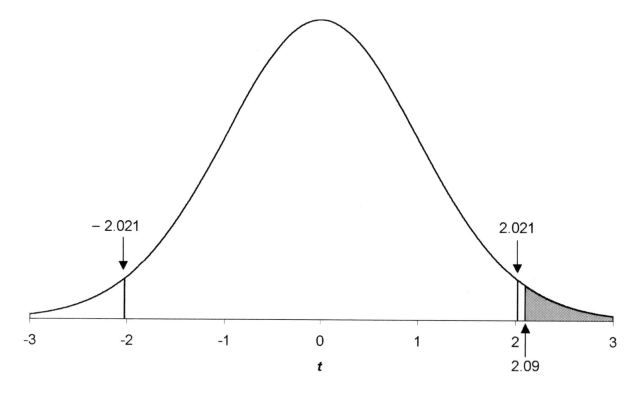

Now let's work through another example, systematically progressing through the steps, using an issue presented earlier in the text. Imagine that we are comparing the mean consideration of future consequences (CFC) scale scores in two populations of second-year students, those who do and those who do not participate in a semester-long program administered by the university career center that focuses on options related to career and graduate studies. At the end of the semester, the following results were obtained for 9 students who participated in the career center program (the experimental group) and 9 students who participated in a program that was unrelated to future employment and education plans (the control group).

	Experimental Group	Control Group
	3.5	4
	4.5	2.5
	3	3.5
	3.5	2
	4	3.5
	3.5	3.5
	3	4
	3.5	3.5
	4	2
M	3.61	3.17
s^2	0.24	0.63
s^2_{pooled}	0.43	
s^2_M	0.05	0.05
$s^2_{difference}$	0.10	
$s_{difference}$	0.31	

Step 1. Identify the populations, distribution, and assumptions.

- The two populations being compared are students who participate in a semester-long program administered by the university career center that focuses on options related to career and graduate studies and students who do not participate in the program.
- The comparison distribution is one of differences between means, and we are conducting an independent-samples t test because we have two independent groups in a between-groups design.
- The assumption that the dependent variable is a scale variable has been met, however we do not know how the participants were selected or if the population data are normally distributed, and we have fewer than 30 observations. We will proceed with caution.

Step 2. State the null and research hypotheses.

Null hypothesis: The mean CFC scores are no different between these two groups: H_0: $\mu_1 = \mu_2$

Research hypothesis: The mean CFC scores are different between these two groups: H_1: $\mu_1 \neq \mu_2$

Step 3. Determine the characteristics of the comparison distribution: Note that these values are shown with the data. Here are the computations in more detail, following the stages outlined in the text on pages 236–238.

(a) Calculate the corrected variance for each group.

X	X − M	(X − M)²
3.5	−0.11	0.01
4.5	0.89	0.79
3	−0.61	0.37
3.5	−0.11	0.01
4	0.39	0.15
3.5	−0.11	0.01
3	−0.61	0.37
3.5	−0.11	0.01
4	0.39	0.15

Y	Y − M	(Y − M)²
4	0.83	0.69
2.5	−0.67	0.45
3.5	0.33	0.11
2	−1.17	1.37
3.5	0.33	0.11
3.5	0.33	0.11
4	0.83	0.69
3.5	0.33	0.11
2	−1.17	1.37

$$s_X^2 = \frac{\Sigma(X - M)^2}{N - 1} = \frac{1.89}{8} = 0.24$$

$$s_Y^2 = \frac{\Sigma(Y - M)^2}{N - 1} = \frac{5}{8} = 0.63$$

(b) Pool the variance estimates. For this stage, we compute pooled variance, or an average of the two variance estimates when they are weighted by a factor of their sample sizes. To weight them, we calculate degrees of freedom:

$$df_X = N - 1 = 9 - 1 = 8 \quad \text{and} \quad df_Y = N - 1 = 9 - 1 = 8$$

$$df_{total} = df_X + df_Y = 8 + 8 = 16$$

$$s_{pooled}^2 = \left(\frac{df_x}{df_{total}}\right)s_X^2 + \left(\frac{df_Y}{df_{total}}\right)s_Y^2 = \left(\frac{8}{16}\right)0.24 + \left(\frac{8}{16}\right)0.63 = 0.43$$

(c) Convert pooled variance to squared standard error for each sample.

$$s_{M_X}^2 = \frac{s_{pooled}^2}{N_X} = \frac{0.43}{9} = 0.05$$

$$s_{M_Y}^2 = \frac{s_{pooled}^2}{N_Y} = \frac{0.43}{9} = 0.05$$

(d) Combine the two variances calculated in (c).

$$s^2_{difference} = s^2_{M_X} + s^2_{M_Y} = 0.05 + 0.05 = 0.1$$

(e) Convert from variance to standard deviation or error units.

$$s_{difference} = \sqrt{s^2_{difference}} = 0.32$$

Step 4. Determine the critical values, or cutoffs. For a two-tailed test with 16 *df* and a *p* level of 0.05, the critical cutoffs are –2.120 and 2.120.

Step 5. Calculate the test statistic.

$$t = \frac{(M_X - M_Y)}{s_{difference}} = \frac{3.61 - 3.17}{0.32} = 1.375$$

Step 6. Make a decision. Because the test statistic, 1.375, fails to exceed the critical cutoff of 2.120, we fail to reject the null hypothesis.

Reporting the Statistics

The test comparing groups on the CFC scale might be reported in a sentence like the following example.

> The comparison of mean CFC scores for the group who experienced the Career Center intervention (*M* = 3.61, *SD* = 0.49) and the group who did not attend meetings (*M* = 3.17, *SD* = 0.794) failed to reach significance, *t*(16) = 1.375, *p* > 0.05.

For the other example, one might write the following:

> The experimental group (*M* = 95, *SD* = 7.75) was statistically different from the control group (*M* = 90, *SD* = 8.94), *t*(40) = 2.09, *p* < 0.05.

If we can obtain exact *p* levels for our statistic, we could also present p_{rep} information.

> Beyond Hypothesis Testing

As you already know, hypothesis testing is only part of the story. We can add great detail by also computing a confidence interval and a measure of effect size.

Confidence Interval

The 95% confidence interval computed to estimate the value of $\mu_X - \mu_Y$ depends upon the two sample means (M_X and M_Y), the standard error of the difference between the sample means ($s_{difference}$), and the critical value of *t* for $N_1 + N_2 - 2$ degrees of freedom and a *p* level determined by subtracting the desired level of confidence from 1 (e.g., $1 - 0.95 = 0.05$).

Following the example used earlier, we will construct a 95% confidence interval for the difference between the mean consideration of future consequences (CFC) scale scores in two populations of second-year students: those who do and those who do not participate in a semester-long program administered by the university career center.

From Appendix B in the text, the critical value of *t* for *df* = 16 and a two-tailed *p* level of 0.05 is 2.12. The lower and upper limits of a 95% confidence interval for the difference between the population means is thus:

$$(M_X - M_Y)_{lower} = -2.12 \, (s_{difference}) + (M_X - M_Y) = -2.12 \, (0.31) + 0.44 = \mathbf{-0.22}$$
$$(M_X - M_Y)_{upper} = +2.12 \, (s_{difference}) + (M_X - M_Y) = 2.12 \, (0.31) + 0.44 = \mathbf{1.1}$$

Because this interval includes the null-hypothesized value of 0 as the difference between the population means, we would fail to reject the null hypothesis and conclude that there is no evidence from this study that the difference between the population mean CFC scale scores is other than 0. Review text pages 242–243 for the steps of confidence interval construction.

> Effect Size

TABLE 10-1.   COHEN'S CONVENTIONS FOR EFFECT SIZES: *d*

Jacob Cohen has published guidelines (or conventions), based on the overlap between two distributions, to help researchers determine whether an effect is small, medium, or large. These numbers are not cutoffs, merely rough guidelines to aid researchers in their interpretation or results.

EFFECT SIZE	CONVENTION	OVERLAP
Small	0.2	85%
Medium	0.5	67%
Large	0.8	53%

Cohen's *d* can be used as a measure of effect size in studies that test the null hypothesis with an independent samples *t* test. Using the group means from the hypothetical study of the effect of the career center program on CFC scale scores, Cohen's *d* is computed as follows:

$$d = \frac{M_X - M_Y}{s_{pooled}} = \frac{3.61 - 3.17}{\sqrt{0.43}} = \frac{0.44}{0.66} = 0.67$$

Please note that the estimate of the population standard deviation is s_{pooled}, the square root of the pooled estimate of the population variance (s^2_{pooled}), rather than the standard error of the difference ($s_{difference}$). This serves as a reminder that effect size is measured in terms of the variability among individual scores rather than the variability among sample means. In this example, the effect size is in the medium-to-large range, despite the inclusion of the null-hypothesized value of the population mean difference in the confidence interval. This effect size value can be included when you report the *t* test.

STUDY QUESTIONS

1. A(n) _____ is used to test whether two population means are equal based on a design in which each participant is assigned to only one condition.
   a. single-sample *t* test
   b. paired-samples *t* test
   c. independent-samples *t* test
   d. *z* test

2. An independent-samples *t* test is used to:
   a. compare the scores in one group of participants to the scores in an unrelated group of participants.
   b. compare the scores obtained under two different conditions in the same group of participants.
   c. test the null hypothesis that two samples of scores have the same mean.
   d. compare the mean of a sample of scores to the mean of a population.

3. Which of the following is the comparison distribution for the independent-samples *t* test?
   a. distribution of sample means
   b. distribution of means of difference scores
   c. distribution of differences between sample means
   d. distribution of differences between population means

4. Which of the following is NOT one of the assumptions that should be met before conducting an independent-samples *t* test?
   a. The dependent variable should be measured on an interval scale.
   b. The populations should be normally distributed.
   c. The samples should have the same number of participants.
   d. The samples should be randomly selected.

5. A psychologist hypothesized that sleep loss affects problem solving. First, she surveyed her large introductory psychology class to determine the number of hours that each student regarded as "a full night's sleep" and then asked how many hours they slept during the previous night. She then gave each student a set of problems to solve in a timed test and counted the number solved correctly by each student. She computed the following statistics on number of problems solved (out of 20) for a group of students who reported a difference of no more than 1 hour between a full night's sleep and how much they slept the previous night (control group: $N = 16$, $M = 16.45$, $s^2 = 24.12$) and a second group who reported getting at least three hours less than a full night's sleep during the previous night (sleep-deprived group: $N = 12$, $M = 12.29$, $s^2 = 19.96$). Which of the following is the most appropriate statement of the null hypothesis?

a. The mean number of problems solved by students who get a "full night's sleep" is not different from the mean number of problems solved by students for whom a full night's sleep time is reduced by at least three hours.

b. The mean number of problems solved by students who get a "full night's sleep" is significantly different from the mean number of problems solved by students for whom a full night's sleep time is reduced by at least three hours.

c. The group of students who reported getting a "full night's sleep" will solve the same number of problems on average as the group of students who reported being sleep-deprived by at least three hours.

d. The group of students who reported getting a "full night's sleep" will solve more problems on average than the group of students who reported being sleep-deprived by at least three hours.

6. A pooled estimate of the population variance (s^2_{pooled}) is determined by:
   a. computing the average of the variances of the samples from two populations.
   b. using the smaller of the two variances of the samples from two populations.
   c. using the larger of the two variances of the samples from two populations.
   d. pooling the two sample variances—that is, adding them together.

7. After obtaining scores from two groups of participants, a researcher computed an estimate of the population variance. Based on the following group statistics, what should her estimate of the population variance be?

	N	Variance
Group 1	11	40
Group 2	21	20

   a. $\left(\dfrac{10}{30}\right)40+\left(\dfrac{20}{30}\right)20=\dfrac{400+400}{30}=\dfrac{800}{30}=26.67$

   b. $\dfrac{40+20}{2}=\dfrac{60}{2}=30$

   c. $\dfrac{40+20}{2}+\dfrac{11+21}{2}=\dfrac{92}{2}=46$

   d. $\dfrac{(11)(40)}{32}+\dfrac{(21)(20)}{32}=\dfrac{440+420}{32}=\dfrac{860}{32}=26.875$

8. For the independent-samples *t* test for independent means, degrees of freedom (df_{total}) are computed as _____.
   a. $(N_1 + N_2 - 1)$
   b. $(N_1 - 1) + (N_2 - 1)$
   c. $(N_1 - 2) + (N_2 - 2)$
   d. $(N_1 + 1) - (N_2 + 1)$

9. The estimated variance of the distribution of differences between means ($s^2_{difference}$) is the:
   a. pooled estimate of the population variance.
   b. sum of the estimated variances of the two distributions of sample means.
   c. weighted average of the estimated variances of the two distributions of sample means.
   d. unweighted average of the estimated variances of the two distributions of sample means.

10. For each of two samples of scores, the squared standard errors are summed before the square root of their sum is taken. What has been computed?
    a. the estimated standard error of the distribution of mean difference scores
    b. the estimated standard error of the distribution of differences between means
    c. the pooled variance as an estimate of the common population variance
    d. the standard deviation of the population

11. You divide the difference between two sample means by $s_{difference}$ to compute:
    a. a pooled estimate of $s^2_{difference}$.
    b. the *p* value of a sample mean difference.
    c. a *t* statistic for an independent-samples *t* test.
    d. a *t* statistic for a paired-samples *t* test.

12. When you have the results of a completed study of two independent samples of scores, you estimate the effect size as the difference between the _____ divided by the _____.
    a. two populations means; population standard deviation
    b. null-hypothesized population mean and the sample mean; standard error of the mean
    c. two sample means; pooled estimate of the population standard deviation
    d. research-hypothesized population mean and the sample mean; standard error of the mean

ANSWERS TO CHAPTER 10 STUDY QUESTIONS

Question Number	Correct Answer	Question Number	Correct Answer
1	c, p. 233	7	a, p. 237
2	a, p. 233	8	b, p. 237
3	c, p. 233	9	b, p. 238
4	c, pp. 234–235	10	b, p. 238
5	a, p. 235	11	c, p. 239
6	a, p. 237	12	c, p. 245

Between-Groups and Within-Groups ANOVA

LEARNING OBJECTIVES

After studying this chapter, you should be able to:

1. Define each of the following terms and provide examples that are not in the text: *ANOVA, F statistic, between-groups variance, within-groups variance, one-way ANOVA, within-groups ANOVA, between-groups ANOVA, homoscedastic, heteroscedastic, source table, grand mean, R^2 post-hoc test,* and *Tukey HSD test.*

2. Explain the analogy between the numerator of the formulas used to compute the z and t statistics and the numerator of the formula used to the compute the F statistic—the between-groups estimate of the population variance. Do the same for the denominator of the formulas used to compute the z and t statistics and the denominator of the for-

mula used to the compute the F statistic—the within-groups estimate of the population variance.

3. Explain the basic distinction between within-groups and between-groups ANOVAs as types of one-way ANOVAs and discuss the assumptions for these tests, including a reference to the distinction between *homoscedastic* and *heteroscedastic* populations (distributions).

4. Discuss the logic that underlies the computation of the ratio of the between-groups variance estimate to the within-group variance estimate in a one-way ANOVA.

5. Explain the source of variability assigned to subjects in a within-groups ANOVA.

6. Explain how to assess effect size for ANOVA using R^2.

7. Discuss the need for for *post-hoc tests* following an ANOVA, and describe Tukey *HSD*.

CHAPTER REVIEW

> **Using the F Distribution With Three or More Samples**

This chapter introduced the **one-way analysis of variance (ANOVA)** for **between-groups** designs. The "one" in "one-way" refers to the inclusion of just one independent variable in the research design. The between-groups one-way ANOVA is like the independent-samples t test in this respect. In fact, the one-way ANOVA may be viewed as an extension of the t test. Whereas the independent-samples t test is limited to two levels of one independent variable, the one-way ANOVA may be used to analyze the data from research designs that include more than two levels of the independent variable. As was true for the t test, the independent variable in an ANOVA must be measured on a nominal scale and the dependent variable must be measured on an interval or ratio scale. The close relation between the independent-samples t test and the between-groups one-way ANOVA is reflected in the fact that squaring the t statistic produces the F statistic that would be computed if the data used to compute the t statistic were subjected to a one-way ANOVA instead—that is, $t^2 = F$, and $t = \sqrt{F}$. As mentioned, the independent-samples t test can not be used to analyze the data from a study with three or more groups of scores, so the comparison is limited to the relatively simple two-sample designs.

The close kinship between the independent-samples t test and the one-way ANOVA for between-groups designs may be illustrated further by a comparison of the formulas used to compute the t and F statistics, respectively:

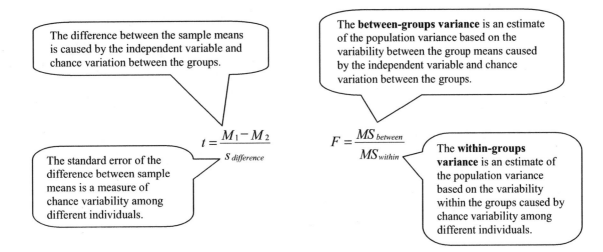

The null hypothesis tested by an ANOVA is that all of the population means are equal. If there are three groups (samples) of scores in a study, then the null hypothesis may be expressed in symbols as follows:

$$H_0 : \mu_1 = \mu_2 = \mu_3$$

The research hypothesis is that the population means are not all the same; that is, at least one of the population means differs from at least one of the others. Note that this statement of the research hypothesis may not be efficiently expressed in symbols.

The F Distribution for Analyzing Variability to Compare Means and the F Table

The formula for the F statistic is a ratio of two sources of variability. The **between-groups variance** computed in the numerator of the formula is a measure of the variability between the sample means. If the null hypothesis is correct, then this source of variability reflects nothing more than the fact that different samples from the same population will have different means just by chance. (Statisticians use the term *sampling error* to refer to this chance variability among sample means.) However, if the research hypothesis is correct, then the between-groups variance is a measure of the variability caused by the effect of the independent variable as well as chance factors. In contrast, the **within-groups variance** is a measure of the spread among scores in the different samples. The major source of differences among scores within any given sample is an enduring source of variability called individual differences; that is, participants differ from on another because of the operation of genetic and environmental influences on behavior. *Unlike* between-groups variance, within-groups variance is unaffected by the status of the null hypothesis.

Understanding the sources of variability that contribute to the between- and within-groups variances should lead you to the following realization:

When the null hypothesis is correct, both the between-groups variance and within-groups variance are products of nothing more than the random variation among scores in the population and have approximately the same value. This means that, on average, the value of the F statistic will be about 1.00 when the null hypothesis is correct. However, if the research hypothesis is correct, then the F statistic will be greater than 1, with its value directly proportional to the magnitude of the differences among the population means. These points may be illustrated as follows:

When the *null* hypothesis is correct:

$$F = \frac{\text{Variability due to } \cancel{\text{the independent variable and}} \text{ chance factors}}{\text{Variability due to chance factors}} = 1$$

When the *research* hypothesis is correct:

$$F = \frac{\text{Variability due to the independent variable and chance factors}}{\text{Variability due to chance factors}} > 1$$

The comparison distribution for an ANOVA is called an F distribution. In contrast to the bell-shape and symmetry of the normal and t distributions, an F distribution has a pronounced positive skew. The positive skew is a consequence of the fact that the F statistic is a ratio of variances. As a ratio of two estimates of the population variance, the F statistic cannot have a negative value, so lower values of this statistic are bunched at the left end of the distribution, exhibiting a kind of floor effect.

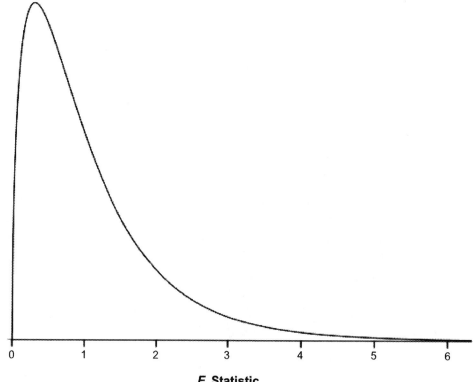

F Statistic

The Language and Assumptions for ANOVA

As mentioned at the beginning of this review, the "one" in the name "one-way ANOVA" refers to the number of independent variables in the design. The practice of naming an ANOVA in terms of the research design for which it is used is further illustrated in the following table.

		Number of Independent Variables	
		1	2 or more
Number of Conditions Experienced by Participants	1	One-Way Between-Groups ANOVA	Factorial Between-Groups ANOVA
	All	One-Way Within-Groups ANOVA	Factorial Within-Groups ANOVA
	More than 1 but not all		Factorial Mixed ANOVA

The factorial ANOVAs listed in the right column of the table are discussed in Chapter 12. The one-way within-groups (also called repeated-measures) ANOVA is also described further in this chapter. For our purposes in this chapter, we will simply note, again, that *one*-way designs, and thus *one*-way ANOVAs, are so-named because they include *one* independent variable. The other major term used to identify an ANOVA refers to whether the study is based on a between-groups design or a within-groups design. This distinction was introduced in Chapter 1 (text page 13) and reintroduced in Chapters 9 and 10 in the descriptions of the independent-samples and paired-samples *t* tests. To review, a between-groups design is one in which each participant is assigned to experience only one condition of the experiment, where a *condition* refers to a level of the independent variable. This means that different groups of participants will be exposed to different levels of the independent variable, and any differences between the scores across the different levels will thus be differences *between* different *groups*. Such differences are analyzed using a one-way **between-groups ANOVA**. In contrast, a within-groups design is one in which each participant experiences all of the conditions of an experiment. Thus each participant is repeatedly measured on the dependent variable— once for each level of the independent variable—and any difference between the levels is thus a difference *within* the same *group*. These differences are analyzed using a one-way **within-groups ANOVA**.

The one-way between-groups ANOVA was described earlier as an extension of the independent-samples t test. The parallels between the t tests and the one-way ANOVAs are further illustrated in the following table.

		Number of Levels of the Independent Variable	
		2	2 or more
Number of Conditions Experienced by Participants	1	Independent-Samples t Test	One-Way Between-Groups ANOVA
	All	Paired-Samples t Test	One-Way Within-Groups ANOVA

The assumptions for the one-way ANOVA are the same as the assumptions for the z and t tests: The dependent variable should be normally distributed and the samples should be randomly selected from populations with equal variances. The results of an ANOVA are relatively robust with respect to a violation of the normality assumption, particularly if the sample size is large enough to invoke the central limit theorem. The criteria for satisfying the equal-variances assumption can be assessed using computer software. As a rough estimate, we can check to see that the largest variance is no more than twice as large as the smallest variance. The terms **homoscedastic** and **heteroscedastic** refer to populations with equal and unequal variances, respectively.

The third assumption, that some method of random sampling is used to select participants, is routinely violated because random sampling is usually impractical. When samples are not randomly selected, the results may be generalized only to individuals who are similar to the participants.

> One-Way Between-Groups ANOVA

Based on the findings of many studies that "mental imagery training has beneficial effects on motor learning and performance,"[1] Ozel, Larue, and Molinaro (2004) "hypothesized that athletes ought to perform mental rotation tasks better than nonathletes. Also, athletes trained to react quickly to con-

---

[1]Quoted material here appeared in original Nolan, S.A., and Heinzen, T.E. (2008). *Statistics for the Behavioral Sciences.* NY: Worth.

stantly changing environments should be faster at processing the information in a mental rotation task than athletes operating in more settled environments" (p. 49). All of the participants stated that they had no experience with mental rotation training or testing of any kind prior to the study.

Step 1. Identify the populations, comparison distribution, and assumptions.

The participants were "36 right-handed male undergraduate unpaid volunteers from the University of Caen between the ages of 18 and 37 years." (p. 52). Ozel et al. tested a "nonathlete" group of 12 male university students who "had to have occupations and spare time activities involving no strong spatial component such as computer sciences, mathematics, or engineering drawing" (p. 53) and compared their scores to two other groups of 12 male students. One group was composed of "athletes engaged in open skills activities" (this group engaged in sporting activities such as handball, rugby, basketball, and soccer, activities that required quick reactions to a changing environment), and the second group "consisted of athletes engaged in closed-skills activities" such as track and field, swimming, gymnastics, and archery—activities that did not require quick responses to a rapidly changing environment (p. 53). Based on these descriptions, we may identify Population 1 as the population of all male nonathletes, aged 18 to 37 years, with limited experience in activities involving visuospatial skills, Population 2 as the population of all male athletes, aged 18 to 37 years, competing in sports requiring quick reactions to rapidly changing environments, and Population 3 as the population of all male athletes, aged 18 to 37 years, competing in sports that involve more settled environments. Please note that the participants do *not* comprise random samples from these populations, so the results of the study may be generalized only with great caution.

The mental rotation task involves simultaneous presentations of two-dimensional representations of three-dimensional geometric figures that are either congruent or mirror images.

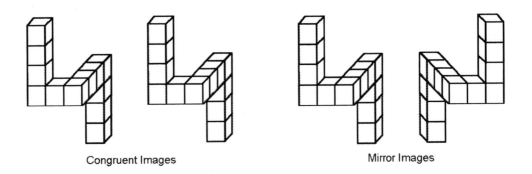

Congruent Images   Mirror Images

Ozel et al. measured mental rotation time as the time (in milliseconds) required for each participant to press one of two response keys to indicate that the images were either the same (congruent) or different (mirror images). The researchers manipulated the number of degrees required to mentally rotate the target stimulus (always the stimulus on the right) as well as the complexity (number of blocks comprising each) of the stimuli. Each participant completed four trials at each of four angles of rotation (45°, 90°, 135°, and 180°) for simple and complex pairs of stimuli. Ozel et al. determined the median response time for each of the four trials determined for each angle and each stimulus type. To simplify the example, we will use fictional data representing the mean of each participant's eight (4 angles of rotation × 2 levels of stimulus complexity) median response times. Although the data are fictional, the group means and standard deviations are very close to those reported by Ozel et al. (2004).

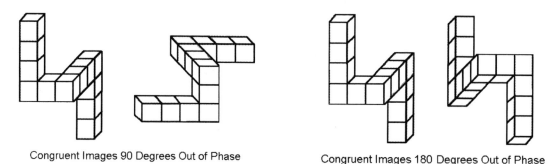

Congruent Images 90 Degrees Out of Phase　　　　Congruent Images 180 Degrees Out of Phase

Step 2. State the null and research hypotheses.

The null hypothesis states that the mean rotation speeds in the three populations are the same. In symbols: $\mu_1 = \mu_2 = \mu_3$. The research hypothesis states that the population means are not all the same; at least one of the population means differs from at least one of the other two.

Step 3. Determine the characteristics of the comparison distribution.

The comparison distribution is an F distribution based on 2 and 33 degrees of freedom. The smaller value is the between-groups degrees of freedom ($df_{between}$). The between-groups degrees of freedom is determined by subtracting 1 from the number of groups of participants: $df_{between} = N_{groups} - 1 = 3 - 1 = 2$. The larger value is the within-groups degrees of freedom (df_{within}). The within-groups degrees of freedom is determined by subtracting the number of groups from the total number of participants: $df_{within} = N - N_{groups} = 36 - 3 = 33$.

Step 4. Determine the critical, or cutoff, values of the test statistic.

The critical value of the F statistic is determined from Table B.3 in the appendix of the text according to three values: the between-groups degrees of freedom ($df_{between}$), the within-groups degrees of freedom (df_{within}), and the significance (p) level. For this analysis, $df_{between} = 2$, $df_{within} = 33$, and the p level is 0.05. A portion of Table B.3 is displayed next to illustrate how to locate the critical value of the F statistic.

WITHIN-GROUPS df	SIGNIF-ICANCE (p) LEVEL	BETWEEN-GROUPS DEGREES OF FREEDOM	
		1	2
30	.01	7.56	5.39
	.05	4.17	3.32
	.10	2.88	2.49

The critical value of the F statistic is located at the intersection of three values: $df_{between}$, df_{within}, and the p level.

Please note that the table does not include 33 as a value of df_{within}, so the next *lower* value, 30, is used. The critical value of F is 3.32.

Step 5. Calculate the test statistic.

The following table displays the raw (fictional) data and the calculations of the sums of squares for each group in the Ozel et al. study of mental rotation in athletes and nonathletes.

Sample	X	$(X - M)^2$	$(M - GM)^2$	$(X - GM)^2$
Open-Skills Athletes $M = 183.08$	252	4749.506944	2149.373	13289.017
	276	8633.506944	2149.373	19398.361
	49	17978.34028	2149.373	7695.149
	178	25.84027778	2149.373	1703.873
	196	166.8402778	2149.373	3513.881
	269	7381.673611	2149.373	17497.469
	44	19344.17361	2149.373	8597.369
	282	9784.506944	2149.373	21105.697
	274	8265.840278	2149.373	18845.249
	41	20187.67361	2149.373	9162.701
	296	12750.17361	2149.373	25369.481
	40	20472.84028	2149.373	9355.145
Closed-Skills Athletes $M = 139.08$	215	5763.340278	5.576	6127.445
	270	17139.17361	5.576	17763.025
	226	7554.506944	5.576	7970.561
	173	1150.340278	5.576	1316.093
	142	8.506944444	5.576	27.857
	53	7410.340278	5.576	7009.373
	44	9040.840278	5.576	8597.369
	40	9817.506944	5.576	9355.145
	188	2392.840278	5.576	2629.433
	25	13015.00694	5.576	12481.805
	265	15855.00694	5.576	16455.245
	28	12339.50694	5.576	11820.473
Nonathletes $M = 88.00$	60	784	2373.833	5886.265
	88	0	2373.833	2373.833
	74	196	2373.833	3934.049
	144	3136	2373.833	52.969
	36	2704	2373.833	10144.921
	47	1681	2373.833	8050.037
	96	64	2373.833	1658.281
	103	225	2373.833	1137.173
	62	676	2373.833	5583.377
	158	4900	2373.833	452.753
	44	1936	2373.833	8597.369
	144	3136	2373.833	52.969

$GM =$ 136.722 $SS_{within} =$ 250665.8333 $SS_{between} =$ 54345.384 $SS_{total} =$ 305011.212

The last three columns of the table include the values that are summed to compute the three sums of squares in the one-way between-groups ANOVA.

- The sum of the values in the column labeled $(X - M)^2$ is the within-groups sum of squares (SS_{within}); that is, $SS_{within} = \Sigma(X - M)^2$.
- The sum of the values in the column labeled $(M - GM)^2$ is the between-groups sum of squares ($SS_{between}$); that is, $SS_{between} = \Sigma(M - GM)^2$. The symbol **GM** represents the **grand mean**, which is computed as the mean score for all of the participants in the study without regard to group membership.
- The sum of the values in the column labeled $(X - GM)^2$ is the total sum of squares (SS_{total}); that is, $SS_{total} = \Sigma(X - GM)^2$.

The first two sums of squares, SS_{within} and $SS_{between}$, are used to compute the two independent estimates of the population variance, the within-groups variance and the between-groups variance, respectively. The total sum of squares (SS_{total}) may be used to check the values computed for SS_{within} and $SS_{between}$; that is, $SS_{total} = SS_{within} + SS_{between}$. The following formula shows the relation between SS_{within} and $SS_{between}$ and the F statistic:

$$F = \frac{MS_{between}}{MS_{within}} = \frac{SS_{between} / df_{between}}{SS_{within} / df_{within}}$$

The sums of squares, degrees of freedom, mean squares, and the F statistic are typically presented in an ANOVA **source table**. The previous source table includes the formulas used to compute the values displayed in the source table that follows for the results of the study of mental rotation.

Source	SS	df	MS	F
Between	$\Sigma(M - GM)^2$	$N_{groups} - 1$	$\dfrac{SS_{between}}{df_{between}}$	$\dfrac{MS_{between}}{MS_{within}}$
Within	$\Sigma(X - M)^2$	$N_{total} - N_{groups}$	$\dfrac{SS_{within}}{df_{within}}$	
Total	$\Sigma(X - GM)^2$	$N_{total} - 1$		

Source	SS	df	MS	F
Between	54345.384	2	27172.692	3.577
Within	250665.8333	33	7595.934	
Total	305011.217	35		

Step 6. Make a decision regarding the status of the null hypothesis.

Before making a decision about our statistical test, we use some of the numbers we have computed to assess whether we met the assumption of equal variances. Once we have computed the variance for each group, we check to see how the smallest and largest variances compare to each other. In this case, the largest variance of 11,794 is more than six times larger than the smallest variance of 1767. We have heteroscedastic groups, so we should proceed with caution when interpreting our findings.

	Open-Skills Athletes	Closed-Skills Athletes	Nonathletes
	4749.51	5763.34	784
	8633.51	17139.17	0
	17978.34	7554.51	196
	25.84	1150.34	3136
	166.84	8.51	2704
Squared Deviations	7381.67	7410.34	1681
	19344.17	9040.84	64
	9784.51	9817.51	225
	8265.84	2392.84	676
	20187.67	13015.01	4900
	12750.17	15855.01	1936
	20472.84	12339.51	3136
Sum of squares:	129740.91	101486.93	19438
$N - 1$	11	11	11
Variance:	11794.63	9226.08	1767.09

With this concern in mind, we examine our F value to see if it exceeds our critical cutoff. Note that when using statistical software, such as *SPSS*, to compute this statistical test, the software will automatically check for homogeneity of variances, and in the case where this assumption is violated, it will make adjustments to the analysis to make it interpretable.

For this test, the null hypothesis may be rejected, because the computed value of the test statistic ($F = 3.577$) is greater than the critical value ($F_{critical} = 3.32$) for $df_{between} = 3$, $df_{within} = 30$, and a p level of 0.05. The results support the research hypothesis: the mean speed of mental rotation is not the same in the populations of open-skills athletes, closed-skills athletes, and nonathletes who spend very little time in activities with a spatial component.

To determine which group means are significantly different from each other, a post-hoc test must be conducted. Post-hoc tests are discussed in the next section, following our review of effect size.

R^2, *the Effect Size for ANOVA*

When comparing more than two groups, we employ a new measure of effect size, R^2. This measure assesses to what extent the variability in the dependent variable is accounted for by the changes of interest (often the researcher's manipulation) in the independent variable.

$$R^2 = \frac{SS_{between}}{SS_{total}} = \frac{54345.384}{305011.217} = 0.178$$

According to Cohen's conventions, this is a large effect size.

Post-Hoc Tests

Some researchers have been outspoken critics of the overall analysis of variance (ANOVA). Their criticism is based on the fact that a rejection of the null hypothesis (which states that all of the population means are equal) is not very informative: The researcher still must determine which of three or more population means differ from each other.

Post-hoc tests are *exploratory* analyses because they are not planned in advance. These tests explore all possible pairwise differences by comparing all unique pairs of group means.

Researchers can choose among several post-hoc tests. Because it is considered neither too liberal nor too conservative, the **Tukey *HSD* test** is widely used and will be illustrated here.

$$HSD = \frac{M_1 - M_2}{\sqrt{\dfrac{MS_{within}}{N}}} = \frac{183.083 - 88}{\sqrt{\dfrac{7595.934}{12}}} = \frac{95.083}{\sqrt{632.995}} = \frac{95.083}{25.159} = 3.779$$

where,

M_1 and M_2 are two group means,

MS_{within} is the within-groups estimate of the population variance from the one-way ANOVA, and

N is the number of participants in each group

If the groups have different numbers of participants, then the harmonic mean of the unequal sample sizes returned by the formula:

$$N' = \frac{N_{groups}}{\sum \dfrac{1}{N}}$$

is substituted for the number in each group (N in the *HSD* formula).

The critical value of the *HSD* statistic is found in Table B.3 (in the appendix of the text) by first locating the column value that corresponds to the number of groups (treatment levels) and then finding the row value that corresponds to the within-groups degrees of freedom (df_{within}) and the *p* level. The value found at the intersection of the appropriate column and row is $HSD_{critical}$. Each computed value of *HSD* that exceeds $HSD_{critical}$ indicates an "honestly significantly different" pair of means.

WITHIN-GROUPS df	SIGNIF-ICANCE (p) LEVEL	k = NUMBER OF TREATMENTS (LEVELS)					
		2	3	4	5	6	7
. . .							
30	.05	2.89	3.49	3.85	4.10	4.30	4.46
	.01	3.89	4.45	4.80	5.05	5.24	5.40

From the table, the critical value of *HSD* for this comparison is 3.49. Because the computed value of *HSD* (3.78) exceeds the critical value, the means are significantly different. Athletes whose competitive activities are mostly of the open-skills type exhibited a significantly higher rate of mental rotation than nonathletes. No other comparisons were significant.

> One-Way Within-Groups ANOVA

Which perfume do you prefer? When you walk through a department store fragrance section and smell several different perfumes, you are experiencing several levels of the independent variable, brand of perfume. As noted in the text, marketing research often uses this approach.

The Benefits of Within-Groups ANOVA

Presenting several perfumes to the same people can allow us to get information about which perfume people prefer, and using the same people helps to control for the variability that each person brings to our research, for example, whether or not their noses are stuffy or they dislike perfume in general. If we can reduce within-groups variability by using the same people across conditions, then the statistical test becomes more sensitive to the variability between groups or, in this case, the differences in preference across perfume brands.

The Six Steps of Hypothesis Testing

Let's review this test by going through a new example. College courses take several different forms, including the large lecture class, the small lecture and discussion class, and the small seminar class. Faculty and administrators are interested in the unique experiences associated with the different classroom settings and dynamics. As students, you probably have some pretty clear preferences based on your own experiences and learning styles. One way to learn more about the differences between these kinds of classes might be to have students experience the different formats and measure the students on some outcome variable, such as satisfaction with the learning experience, amount learned, level of active participation, or some other criterion believed to be important.

Following are some fictional data about class format and level of active participation for 6 students. Active participation was measured as the number of vocal contributions in a semester, and inclusion in our fictional study is limited to students who had a minimum of one contribution (we do not want to have all zeros for the large lecture group!).

Participant	Large Lecture	Small Lecture/Discussion	Small Seminar
1	4	7	29
2	6	7	26
3	2	11	24
4	3	9	21
5	1	6	19
6	2	5	31

Step 1. Identify the populations, distribution, and assumptions.

1. The populations being compared are students who participate in lecture classes, small lecture/discussion classes, and small seminars.
2. The comparison distribution is an F distribution because we are comparing more than two groups. The hypothesis test is a one-way within-groups ANOVA.
3. The assumptions
   - The participants were not randomly selected.
   - We do not know if the underlying distributions are normal, but we can examine the sample data for skew.
   - With real data, we would use statistical software to check the variances for homoscedasticity
   - We don't have information about how the class experiences were ordered, so we don't know if that is an issue here.

Note that we have not met or are not sure about whether we met the assumptions for this test. ANOVA stands up relatively well to violations of these assumptions, but we should always proceed with caution.

Step 2. State the null and research hypotheses.

Null Hypothesis: The mean CFC scores are no different between these groups. H_0: $\mu_1 = \mu_2 = \mu_3$.

Research Hypothesis: The average participation levels across these three class types will not be the same.

Step 3. Determine the characteristics of the comparison distribution. We must calculate four different degrees of freedom for this test.

$$df_{between} = N_{groups} - 1 = 3 - 1 = 2$$

$$df_{subjects} = n - 1 = 6 - 1 = 5$$

$$df_{within} = (df_{between})(df_{subjects}) = (2)(5) = 10$$

$$df_{total} = df_{between} + df_{subjects} + df_{within} = 2 + 5 + 10 = 17$$

When referencing the table, we will use 2 and 10 degrees of freedom.

Step 4. Determine the critical values, or cutoffs. For this test with 2 and 10 df and a p level of 0.05, the critical cutoff is 4.10.

Step 5. Calculate the test statistic. Here are all the calculations that go into reaching our final test statistic.

Calculate the total sums of squares: SS_{total}.

$$SS_{total} = \Sigma(X - GM)^2 = 1766.50$$

	X	**(X − GM)**	**(X − GM)²**
Large Lecture	4	−7.833	61.356
	6	−5.833	34.024
	2	−9.833	96.688
	3	−8.833	78.022
	1	−10.833	117.354
	2	−9.833	96.688
Small Lecture	7	−4.833	23.358
	7	−4.833	23.358
	11	−0.833	0.694
	9	−2.833	8.026
	6	−5.833	34.024
	5	−6.833	46.690
Small Seminar	29	17.167	294.706
	26	14.167	200.704
	24	12.167	148.036
	21	9.167	84.034
	19	7.167	51.366
	31	19.167	367.374
GM = 11.833			Σ = 1766.50

Calculate the between-groups sums of squares.

$$SS_{between} = \Sigma(X - GM)^2 = 1621.0$$

	X	**Group Mean**	*(M – GM)²*	*(M – GM)²*
Large Lecture	4	3	–8.833	78.022
	6	3	–8.833	78.022
	2	3	–8.833	78.022
	3	3	–8.833	78.022
	1	3	–8.833	78.022
	2	3	–8.833	78.022
Small Lecture	7	7.5	–4.333	18.775
	7	7.5	–4.333	18.775
	11	7.5	–4.333	18.775
	9	7.5	–4.333	18.775
	6	7.5	–4.333	18.775
	5	7.5	–4.333	18.775
Small Seminar	29	25	13.167	173.370
	26	25	13.167	173.370
	24	25	13.167	173.370
	21	25	13.167	173.370
	19	25	13.167	173.370
	31	25	13.167	173.370
GM = 11.833				Σ = 1621

Calculate the subjects sums of squares.

$$SS_{subjects} = \Sigma(M_{participant} - GM)^2 = 45.825$$

	Student	X	Student Mean	$(M_{student} - GM)$	$(M_{student} - GM)^2$
Large Lecture	1	4	13.333	1.500	2.250
	2	6	13	1.167	1.362
	3	2	12.333	0.500	0.250
	4	3	11	−0.833	0.694
	5	1	8.667	−3.166	10.024
	6	2	12.667	0.834	0.696
Small Lecture	1	7	13.333	1.500	2.250
	2	7	13	1.167	1.362
	3	11	12.333	0.500	0.250
	4	9	11	−0.833	0.694
	5	6	8.667	−3.166	10.024
	6	5	12.667	0.834	0.696
Small Seminar	1	29	13.333	1.500	2.250
	2	26	13	1.167	1.362
	3	24	12.333	0.500	0.250
	4	21	11	−0.833	0.694
	5	19	8.667	−3.166	10.024
	6	31	12.667	0.834	0.696
GM = 11.833					Σ= 45.825

Calculate the within-groups sums of squares.

$$SS_{within\text{-}groups} = SS_{total} - SS_{between} - SS_{subjects} = 1766.50 - 1621 - 45.825 = 99.675$$

Now we calculate the rest of the source table using the equations provided.

$$MS_{between} = \frac{SS_{between}}{df_{between}} = \frac{1621}{2} = 810.50$$

$$MS_{subjects} = \frac{SS_{subjects}}{df_{subjects}} = \frac{45.825}{5} = 9.165$$

$$MS_{within} = \frac{SS_{within}}{df_{within}} = \frac{99.675}{10} = 9.967$$

$$F_{between} = \frac{MS_{between}}{MS_{within}} = \frac{810.50}{9.967} = 81.318$$

$$F_{subjects} = \frac{MS_{subjects}}{MS_{within}} = \frac{9.165}{9.967} = 0.919$$

Source	SS	df	MS	F
Between-groups	1621	2	810.50	81.318
Subjects	45.825	5	9.165	0.919
Within-groups	99.675	10	9.967	
Total	1766.50	17		

Step 6. Make a decision. Because the test statistic, 81.318, exceeds the critical cutoff, we reject the null hypothesis. It appears that there is a difference in participation level across these three class types.

R^2, the Effect Size for ANOVA

Now we calculate the effect size, with a modification to the formula we used earlier. This new formula removes the variability accounted for by subjects.

$$R^2 = \frac{SS_{between}}{(SS_{total} - SS_{subjects})} = \frac{1621}{(1766.50 - 45.825)} = 0.942$$

According to the conventions presented in Table 11-12 in the text, this is a large effect size, with approximately 94% of the variability in participation level explained by the type of class in which students were observed.

Tukey HSD

Post-hoc tests can now tell us where significant differences occurred between the three class formats studied. We can compute our post-hoc tests for this ANOVA just as we did for the between-groups ANOVA. We start with a calculation of standard error.

$$s_M = \sqrt{\frac{MS_{within}}{N}} = \sqrt{\frac{9.967}{6}} = 1.289$$

Now let's compare the class formats. Large lecture ($M = 3$) compared to small lecture ($M = 7.5$):

$$HSD = \frac{3 - 7.5}{1.289} = -3.49$$

Large lecture ($M = 3$) compared to seminar ($M = 25$):

$$HSD = \frac{3 - 25}{1.289} = -17.07$$

Small lecture ($M = 7.5$) compared to seminar ($M = 25$):

$$HSD = \frac{7.5 - 25}{1.289} = -13.58$$

According to the table in the Appendix, the critical cutoffs for q when comparing 3 treatments with 10 df within groups, using a two-tailed test with a p level of 0.05, are -3.88 and 3.88. When comparing the class formats, we found a statistically significant difference in participation level between seminar classes and both large lectures and small lectures. However, no statistical difference was found between small and large lectures.

As the authors of the text note, the results of a study such as this fictional one about class formats and levels of participation often lead to more questions and greater curiosity. Does class format have consequences for learning? How big is the statistics class you are in right now, and does the size have an impact on you? Statistics can help you explore the possible answers.

REFERENCE

Ozel, S., Larue, J., & Molinaro, C. (2004). Relation between sport and spatial imagery: Comparison of three groups of participants. *The Journal of Psychology, 138*(1), 49–63.

STUDY QUESTIONS

1. Which one of the following best expresses what an analysis of variance is about?
   a. a comparison of two different ways of estimating population variances
   b. a comparison of estimates of the true values of three or more population means
   c. a comparison of estimates of the true values of three or more population variances
   d. a comparison of three or more estimates of the true value of a single population mean

2. An analysis of variance is conducted to determine whether the _____ differ more than you would expect if the null hypothesis were true.
   a. means of the samples
   b. variances of the samples
   c. means of the populations
   d. variances of the populations

3. Although an analysis of variance is conducted to answer the question of whether the _____ of the samples differ more than you would expect if the null hypothesis were true, this question is addressed by analyzing _____.
   a. means; variances
   b. variances; means
   c. variances; sample sizes
   d. variances; population variances

4. The **within-groups variance** tells you how much:
   a. the means vary among the samples.
   b. the means vary among the populations.
   c. the scores within each sample (group) vary.
   d. each sample mean differs from the true population mean.

5. The variances (s^2) for each of five (5) groups of 20 scores are as follows: 64, 121, 144, 169, and 81. If you averaged these five variances, you would have computed the:
   a. between-groups estimate of the population variance.
   b. within-groups estimate of the population variance.
   c. population variance.
   d. F statistic.

6. Which one of the following statements most accurately describes the relation between the F statistic and the t statistic?
   a. The two statistics are not related, either to each other, or to any other statistic.
   b. Both statistics are related to the z statistic, but they are not related to each other.
   c. For a study of two independent groups of participants, the square root of the F statistic is equal to the t statistic.
   d. For a study of any number of independent groups of participants, the square root of the F statistic is equal to the t statistic.

7. A(n) _____ ANOVA is a hypothesis test in which there are more than two samples, and each sample is composed of different participants.
   a. one-way
   b. within-groups
   c. repeated-measures
   d. between-groups

8. Which of the following is *not* an assumption for an analysis of variance?
   a. The populations should follow a normal curve.
   b. The variances of the populations should be equal.
   c. The samples should have the same number of participants.
   d. The participants should be randomly selected from the population.

9. Populations that have the same variance are called _____ populations.
   a. normal
   b. heteroscedastic
   c. homoscedastic
   d. heterogeneous

10. How are the within-groups variance and the status of the null hypothesis related, if at all?
    a. If the null hypothesis is true, then the within-groups variance will be larger than it would be if the null hypothesis is false.
    b. If the null hypothesis is true, then the within-groups variance will be smaller than it would be if the null hypothesis is false.
    c. The relation between the within-groups variance and the status of the null hypothesis depends on the size of the samples in the study.
    d. Within-groups variance and the status of the null hypothesis are not related.

11. An analysis of variance (ANOVA) is commonly used to test the null hypothesis that:
    a. three or more population means are equal.
    b. three or more population means differ from each other.
    c. at least one of three or more population means differs from the others.
    d. the variance between different groups is equal to the variance within each of the groups.

12. You are interested in comparing four methods of teaching. You randomly assign 20 students to each of the four methods and then administer a standardized test at the end of the study. The null hypothesis that you are interested in testing is:
    a. teaching method and intelligence are independent in the population.
    b. the mean standardized test scores differ for the four teaching methods.
    c. the mean standardized test scores are the same for the four teaching methods.
    d. the sample means for the four groups assigned to the different teaching methods are equal.

13. In a comparison of the average number of hours worked per week for five different levels of education (e.g., no HS degree, HS graduate, some college, college graduate, graduate degree), the research hypothesis would state that:
    a. there is no difference in the average hours worked for people in the five education categories.
    b. any differences in the average hours worked in the five groups are attributable to chance.
    c. the means for the different levels of education are not all the same in the population.
    d. the population means for all five levels of education are the same.

14. In an analysis of variance, the between-groups degrees of freedom is computed as the:
    a. sum of the degrees of freedom ($n - 1$) for each group.
    b. total number of participants in the study (N) minus 1.
    c. number of scores in each group (n) minus 1.
    d. number of groups minus 1.

15. In an analysis of variance, the within-groups degrees of freedom is computed as the:
    a. sum of the degrees of freedom ($n - 1$) for each group.
    b. total number of participants in the study (N) minus 1.
    c. number of scores in each group (n) minus 1.
    d. number of groups minus 1.

16. A researcher reported the following results of a study conducted to investigate whether there are differences among the anxiety test scores recorded for college students who have been diagnosed with panic disorder, generalized anxiety disorder, and social phobia. A group of students with no diagnosis of an anxiety disorder was included for comparison purposes.

Group	M	SD	n
Panic Disorder	24	5	22
Generalized Anxiety Disorder	20	9	34
Social Phobia	18	6	29
No Diagnosis	10	8	30

The comparison distribution for an analysis of the data in the table just shown is an F distribution with _____ degrees of freedom.
    a. 3 and 111
    b. 4 and 115
    c. 3 and 112
    d. 21, 33, 28, and 29

17. A(n) _____ is used to locate a critical value of the F statistic and to determine how extreme a computed F statistic must be in order to reject the null hypothesis at a given p level.
    a. F distribution
    b. normal distribution
    c. F table
    d. ANOVA table

18. Excerpt from the F Table:

Within-Groups df	Significance (p) Level	Between-Groups Degrees of Freedon					
		1	2	3	4	5	6
10	0.01	10.05	7.56	6.55	6.00	5.64	5.39
	0.05	4.97	4.10	3.71	3.48	3.33	3.22
	0.10	3.29	2.93	2.73	2.61	2.52	2.46
11	0.01	9.65	7.21	6.22	5.67	5.32	5.07
	0.05	4.85	3.98	3.59	3.36	3.20	3.10
	0.10	3.23	2.86	2.66	2.54	2.45	2.39
12	0.01	9.33	6.93	5.95	5.41	5.07	4.82
	0.05	4.75	3.89	3.49	3.26	3.11	3.00
	0.10	3.18	2.81	2.61	2.48	2.40	2.33
13	0.01	9.07	6.70	5.74	5.21	4.86	4.62
	0.05	4.67	3.81	3.41	3.18	3.03	2.92
	0.10	3.14	2.76	2.56	2.43	2.35	2.28

If the null hypothesis is tested at the 0.01 p level, what is the critical value of the F statistic for an ANOVA with 4 groups, each with 15 participants?
    a. 3.89
    b. 5.21
    c. 5.74
    d. The value is not in the table.

19. In a test of the null hypothesis that three populations have identical means, a researcher computed the value of an F statistic to be 3.14 based on the scores obtained from 3 groups of 21 participants (63 participants in all). If the p level was set at 0.05, which of the following is the correct decision based on the critical cutoff listed?
    a. The null hypothesis should be rejected because $F(3, 21) = 3.07$.
    b. The null hypothesis should not be rejected because $F(2, 21) = 3.47$.
    c. The null hypothesis should be rejected because $F(3, 60) = 2.76$.
    d. The null hypothesis should not be rejected because $F(2, 60) = 3.15$.

20. An F distribution is:
    a. bell-shaped like a normal curve.
    b. positively skewed.
    c. negatively skewed.
    d. shaped like a rectangle.

21. An F statistic is a ratio of an estimate of the population variance based on variation among the _____ to an estimate of the population variance based on variation among the _____.
    a. scores in each sample; means of each sample
    b. means of each sample; scores in each sample
    c. scores in each population; means of each population
    d. means of each population; scores in each population

22. The F statistic is a ratio of the:
    a. within-groups to the between-groups variance estimate.
    b. between-groups to the within-groups variance estimate.
    c. mean of the group means to the overall (grand) mean.
    d. between-groups degrees of freedom to the within-groups degrees of freedom.

23. The between-groups variance is based solely on the variability among the:
    a. means of each sample.
    b. scores in each sample.
    c. scores in each population.
    d. means in each population.

24. Consider the following figure from the text (Figure 11-3):

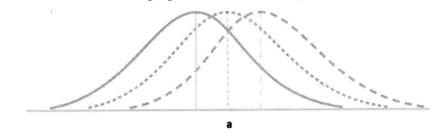

a

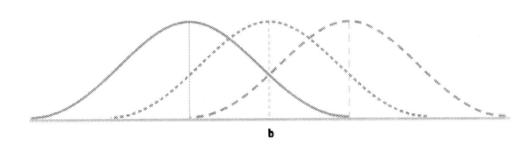

b

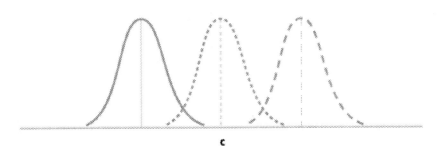

c

For which of the three sets of distributions is the ratio of between-groups variance to within-groups variance largest?
   a. the top set of distributions (a)
   b. the middle set of distributions (b)
   c. the bottom set of distributions (c)
   d. The ratio is approximately the same in the three sets of distributions.

25. The within-groups variance and the between-groups variance will be about the same when:
   a. the null hypothesis is true.
   b. the research hypothesis is true.
   c. either the null or the research hypothesis is true, depending on the number of groups.
   d. False premise: The within-groups and between-groups variance estimates are never approximately the same.

26. The ratio of the between-groups variance to the within-groups variance is _____ when the null hypothesis is true.
    a. 0
    b. approximately 1
    c. extremely large
    d. undefined

27. Which one of the following is *not* included in an analysis of variance **source table**?
    a. SS_{total}
    b. $df_{between}$
    c. n
    d. F

28. Which of the following is the sum of the squared deviations of each score from the grand mean?
    a. SS_{within}
    b. $SS_{between}$
    c. SS_{total}
    d. MS_{within}

29. Which of the following completely ignore(s) the group a score is in?
    a. $SS_{between}$
    b. SS_{within}
    c. SS_{total}
    d. $SS_{between}$ and SS_{within}

30. In an analysis of variance, the **grand mean** is:
    a. the mean of all of the scores without regard to group membership.
    b. the mean of the variances of each group.
    c. the ratio of $MS_{between}$ to MS_{within}.
    d. not computed unless the research hypothesis is true.

31. Which one of the following formulas expresses the fact that $SS_{total} = SS_{within} + SS_{between}$?
    a. $\Sigma(X - GM)^2 = \Sigma(X - M)^2 + \Sigma(M - GM)^2$
    b. $\Sigma(M - GM)^2 = \Sigma(X - M)^2 + \Sigma(X - GM)^2$
    c. $\Sigma(X - M)^2 = \Sigma(X - GM)^2 + \Sigma(M - GM)^2$
    d. $\Sigma(X - M)^2 = \Sigma(M - GM)^2 + \Sigma(X - GM)^2$

32. The sum of the squared deviations of each score from its group mean is the:
    a. within-groups sum of squares (SS_{within}).
    b. between-groups sum of squares ($SS_{between}$).
    c. total sum of squares (SS_{total}).
    d. within-groups mean square (SS_{within}).

33. The sum of the squared deviations of each score's group mean from the grand mean is the:
    a. within-groups sum of squares (SS_{within}).
    b. between-groups sum of squares ($SS_{between}$).
    c. total sum of squares (SS_{total}).
    d. within-groups variance (MS_{within}).

34. An incomplete source table for an analysis of variance:

Source	SS	df	MS	F
Between Groups	150.000	3		
Within Groups	600.000	50		
Total	750.000	53		

Use the information in the source table to determine which of the following is $MS_{between}$.
    a. 150
    b. 50
    c. 6
    d. 600

35. If $SS_{between} = 150$, $SS_{within} = 600$, $df_{between} = 3$, and $df_{within} = 50$, what is the value of the F statistic?
    a. 4.167
    b. 4
    c. 0.25
    d. 0.06

36. Which one of the following statements regarding post hoc tests is most accurate?
    a. A post-hoc test may be conducted only after the result of an analysis of variance permits a rejection of the null hypothesis.
    b. A post-hoc test may be conducted only after the result of an analysis of variance lead us to fail to reject the null.
    c. Post-hoc tests require some adjustment of the probability of committing a Type I error.
    d. Post-hoc tests require some adjustment of the probability of committing a Type II error.

37. The Tukey *HSD* test is:
    a. a test of effect size.
    b. a commonly used post-hoc test.
    c. another name for an independent-samples *t* test.
    d. the only post-hoc test that may be used with unequal sample sizes.

38. In a _____ design, each participant experiences all levels of the independent variable.
    a. within-groups
    b. between-groups
    c. correlational
    d. market-research

39. For a one-way within-groups ANOVA, a new source of variability is computed. The variability is accounted for by the:
    a. design.
    b. within-group differences.
    c. subjects.
    d. treatment manipulation.

40. One measure of effect size for ANOVA is:
    a. beta.
    b. R^2.
    c. p^2.
    d. Bonferroni.

ANSWERS TO CHAPTER 11 STUDY QUESTIONS

Question Number	Correct Answer
1	a, pp. 257–258
2	a, pp. 257–258
3	a, pp. 257–258
4	c, p. 258
5	b, p. 258
6	c, p. 259
7	d, p. 259
8	c, p. 260
9	c, p. 260
10	d, p. 262
11	a, p. 262
12	c, p. 262
13	c, p. 262
14	d, p. 263
15	a, p. 263
16	a, p. 263
17	c, p. 263
18	d, pp. 263–264 [The between-groups df = the number of groups $- 1 = 4 - 1 = 3$, and the within-groups df = the number of participants in each group minus $1 = 15 - 1 + 15 - 1 + 15 - 1 + 15 - 1 = (4)(14) = 56$; alternatively, df_{within} = the total number of participants minus the number of groups $= 60 - 4 = 56$.]

Question Number	Correct Answer
19	d, pp. 263–264
20	b, p. 264
21	b, p. 265
22	b, p. 265
23	a, pp. 265–267
24	c, pp. 266–267
25	a, p. 267
26	b, p. 267
27	c, p. 267
28	c, pp. 268–269
29	c, pp. 268–272
30	a, p. 269
31	a, pp. 269–272
32	a, p. 270–271
33	b, p. 272
34	b, p. 273
35	a, pp. 273–274
36	a, pp. 276–277
37	b, p. 277
38	a, pp. 281–282
39	c, p. 286
40	b, pp. 288 and 275

CHAPTER TWELVE

Two-Way ANOVA

CHAPTER OUTLINE

Two-Way ANOVA
- Why We Use a Two-Way ANOVA
- The More Specific Vocabulary of Two-Way ANOVAs
- Two Main Effects and an Interaction

Understanding Interactions in ANOVA
- Interactions and Public Policy
- Interpreting Interactions

Conducting a Two-Way Between-Groups ANOVA
- The Six Steps of Two-Way ANOVA
- Identifying Four Sources of Variability in Two-Way ANOVA
- Effect Size for Two-Way ANOVA

LEARNING OBJECTIVES

After studying this chapter, you should be able to:

1. Define each of the following terms and provide examples that are not in the text: *two-way ANOVA*, *factorial analysis of variance*, *mixed-design ANOVA*, *factor*, *cell*, *main effect*, *interaction*, *quantitative interaction*, *qualitative interaction*, and *marginal means*.

2. Distinguish between a one-way and a two-way ANOVA and explain the advantages of a two-way ANOVA over a one-way ANOVA.

3. Explain the difference between a 2 × 2 and a 3 × 2 factorial ANOVA as well as the difference between the between-groups and within-groups versions of each. In addition, you should be able to determine the number of cells in a two-way ANOVA identified in this way.

4. Provide explanations and examples that distinguish between (a) main and interaction effects, (b) quantitative and qualitative interactions, and (c) the relative importance of main and interaction effects.

5. Construct tables of cell and marginal means for a two-way ANOVA and manipulate the means to indicate any combination of main and interaction effects that you may then depict in bar graphs.

6. Describe the six steps of the hypothesis-testing procedure as it applies to a two-way ANOVA and explain the elements of an ANOVA source table that results from the analysis.
7. Evaluate effect size for two-way ANOVA.

CHAPTER REVIEW

> Two-Way ANOVA

This chapter introduces the **two-way analysis of variance (ANOVA)** as an extension of the one-way ANOVA described in Chapter 11. The "two" in the name of the ANOVA refers to the inclusion of two independent variables (called **factors**) in the design and analysis. The two-way ANOVA, in turn, is a member of the class of analyses called factorial ANOVAs. A **factorial ANOVA** is used to analyze the data from a factorial design. The most commonly used factorial design is called a *between-groups design*. This term was introduced in Chapter 1 and reviewed in Chapters 10 and 11. In a between-groups design, participants are randomly assigned to experience only one level of one factor. The most basic factorial ANOVA, and the one discussed at length in this chapter, is a two-way ANOVA for a between-groups design; so this ANOVA is most completely described as a *two-way between-groups ANOVA*.

All between-groups factorial designs include:
- two or more independent variables (factors), each of which has two or more levels.
- one interval- or ratio-scaled dependent variable, which is the same for all participants.
- conditions or **cells** defined as the combination of one level of one factor with one level of the other factor(s); each cell identifies a different group of participants.
- random assignment of 10–20 participants to each cell of the design.
- one possible **main effect** of each factor and one possible **interaction** for each unique combination of factors. *These are further described later in this discussion.*
- a name specified by the number of factors, and the number of levels of each factor. For example, a **2 × 2 design (read "two-by-two")** has two factors and two levels in each one; a 3 × 2 design also has two factors, with 3 levels of the first factor and 2 levels of the second factor; a 3 × 2 × 3 design has 3 factors, and so forth.
- a number of cells determined by the product of the number of levels of each factor. For example, in a 2 × 2 design, there are (2) (2) = 4 cells; in a 3 × 2 design, there are (3) (2) = 6 cells; in a 3 × 2 × 3 design, there are (3) (2) (3) = 18 cells, etc.

- at least three null hypotheses that are tested by a factorial ANOVA.
- The ANOVA is identified by the number of factors in the design: if there are two factors, the ANOVA is termed a "two-way" ANOVA; if there are three factors, the ANOVA is termed a "three-way" ANOVA, etc.

In a 2 × 2 factorial design, the factors may be generically identified as Factor A and Factor B. Each factor has two levels, which may be designated using the notation A_1, A_2, B_1, and B_2. Using this notation, there are four unique combinations of levels (cells) in a 2 × 2 design: A_1B_1, A_1B_2, A_2B_1, and A_2B_2. These are identified in the following annotated figure.

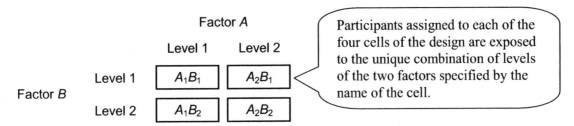

The influence of any single factor on the dependent variable is called a main effect. Thus, a **main effect** occurs when the different levels of one factor produce significantly different effects on the dependent variable, *irrespective of the other factor(s)*. For example, a main effect of Factor A occurs when the mean of level A_1 (the first column mean) differs significantly from the mean of level A_2 (the second column mean), ignoring the specific cell means for the levels of Factor B. Similarly, a main effect of Factor B is observed when the mean of level B_1 (the first row mean) differs significantly from the mean of level B_2 (the second row mean), ignoring the specific cell means for the levels of Factor A. The following figure illustrates the cell, row, and column means for the generic 2 × 2 ANOVA. The row and column means are also called **marginal means**; the marginal means are compared in a test of main effects.

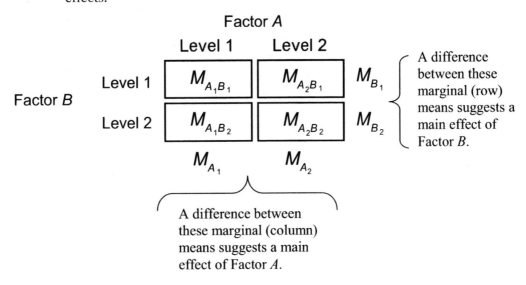

There are as many potential main effects as there are factors in a factorial design. For example, in a 2 × 2 design there are two possible main effects: using conventional notation, we would say that there may be a "main effect of *A*," a "main effect of *B*," or "main effects for both *A* and *B*."

A factorial ANOVA is more efficient than a one-way ANOVA in that it provides simultaneous tests of the effects of more than one factor. In addition, and more importantly, a factorial ANOVA includes a test of whether the combination of the factors influences the dependent variable differently than is apparent when the factors are considered independently. In other words, a factorial ANOVA provides an opportunity to examine a possible interaction between the factors by considering their effects in combination. As defined in the text, an **interaction** is observed "when the two independent variables have an effect in combination that we do not see when we examine each independent variable on its own" (text page 304).

> Understanding Interactions in ANOVA

Interactions may be described as quantitative or qualitative, according to whether the effects of the levels of one factor vary in magnitude or vary in direction over the levels of the other factor. A quantitative interaction occurs when the quantity or size of the influence of one variable changes over levels of the second variable. A qualitative interaction occurs when the effect actually changes direction. Let's illustrate these interactions by working through the impact gender and age might have on income. Imagine that there is an income gap, with men earning more than women on average. A quantitative interaction would occur if the size of the gap changes with age—say, if the gap is $8,000 on average for younger workers and $28,000 on average for older workers. A qualitative interaction would occur if the gap changed directions, with women earning more than men when younger and men earning more than women when older.

Researchers typically conduct studies based on a factorial design because they are interested in interaction effects. Put another way, the primary rationale for employing a factorial design is at least one research hypothesis that predicts an interaction effect. However, even in the absence of any interaction effects, the factorial design is valued as an efficient method of analyzing the main effects of two or more factors, because the design is, in effect, a combination of two or more one-way designs conducted at the same time.

Let's look at interactions more closely. In the next section, some data are presented about shampoo preference and gender. Males and females were asked to rate their degree of liking from 1 (strong dislike) to 10 (strong liking) of two shampoos. The cell and marginal means for that example are presented here.

	Best-Selling Shampoo	New Shampoo	Marginal Means
Females	5.50	9.25	7.38
Males	5.75	6.50	6.13
Marginal Means	5.63	7.88	6.75

To examine the main effect of gender, we create a new table. From these numbers, we can see that females gave higher ratings of liking than males, indicating a possible main effect for gender.

	Marginal Means
Females	7.38
Males	6.13

To examine the main effect of shampoo, we examine the shampoo marginal means. These numbers reveal that, on average, the new shampoo was rated higher than the best-selling shampoo, perhaps indicating a main effect for product familiarity or novelty in this case.

	Best-Selling Shampoo	New Shampoo
Marginal Means	5.63	7.88

To examine the interaction, we examine the pattern of means:

	Best-Selling Shampoo	New Shampoo
Females	5.50	9.25
Males	5.75	6.50

Here we can see that the increase in liking across product type is greater for females than for males, perhaps indicating a significant interaction. This interaction would be a quantitative interaction because its size changes across the two genders. As indicated in the text, creating visual displays of such means can often help reveal main effects and interactions to the viewer. Also, there is no substitute for the actual statistical test, which we will now perform.

> Conducting a Two-Way Between-Groups ANOVA

Now we'll be reviewing our six steps of hypothesis testing for a two-way ANOVA. Let's start with a simple example that will guide us through the entire process. Imagine that we are working for a company that is developing a new type of shampoo. We want to figure out if people prefer the shampoo compared to the current best-seller. We also want to figure out if we should market the shampoo to men or women, and so we want to see if there's a difference in preference for the shampoo between genders. In our marketing study, male and female testers were either given the new shampoo or the best-seller and after using the shampoo, we asked them to rate how much they liked it on a scale of 1 (hated it) to 10 (best shampoo ever). For the purposes of our example, we'll only put four testers in each group but know that if this was a real study, we'd probably want to use more than only 16 total testers!

Experimental Condition	Data for Testers	Mean Liking of Product
Females, Best-Seller	5, 5, 6, 6	5.50
Females, New Product	9, 9, 9, 10	9.25
Males, Best-Seller	4, 5, 6, 8	5.75
Males, New Product	6, 6, 7, 7	6.50
		Grand Mean (GM) = 6.75

Now that we have our data in hand, let's go through the steps necessary for the ANOVA.

Step 1. Identify the populations, distributions, and assumptions.

For our example, we have four populations with four raters in each population. Population 1 refers to females who received the best-seller. Population 2 refers to females who received the new product. Population 3 refers to males who received the best-seller. Lastly, population 4 refers to males who received the new product. Now would also be a good opportunity to discuss our independent variables. Our first independent variable is gender with two levels (male or female), and our second independent variable is the product type (best-seller or new product).

We now need to look at the distribution to which we will compare our sample. Because we have more than 2 groups, we will need to use the F distribution, which means we'll use an ANOVA. Because we're looking at two independent variables, we know that this is a two-way ANOVA. Because our groups are not related to one another in any way, we also know that this is a between-groups ANOVA.

Our assumptions in a two-way ANOVA are the same as our one-way ANOVA. First, our sample should be randomly selected. Second, the populations should be normally distributed. Third, the population variances should be equal or show **homoscedasticity**. For our marketing study, our sample is not random because the testers come from our pool of product testers rather than the general population. We also don't know about the normal distribution or homoscedasticity of our population. So, we want to be cautious about any conclusions that we make (although with only three testers in each group, we would want to be very cautious no matter what).

Step 2. State the null and research hypotheses.

For a two-way ANOVA we have three sets of hypotheses—one for each of the main effects and one for the interaction. For the main effects, in our case because we have two levels in each of our two independent variables, we can say that the two levels are not equal:

Gender Main Effect

Null Hypothesis: On average, males and females will not differ in shampoo liking, $H_0 = \mu_m = \mu_f$.

Research Hypothesis: On average, males and females will differ in shampoo liking, $H_1 = \mu_m \neq \mu_f$.

Shampoo Main Effect

Null Hypothesis: On average, there will be no difference in liking between the best-seller and the new product, $H_0 = \mu_b = \mu_n$.

Research Hypothesis: On average, the best-seller will differ in liking than the new product, $H_1 = \mu_b \neq \mu_n$.

If we had more than two levels in any of our independent variables, our research hypothesis would state that any two levels of the independent variable are not equal to one another.

For our interaction, we state the hypotheses in words rather than symbols. The null hypothesis is that the effect of one independent variable does not depend on the level of the other independent variable, whereas the research hypothesis is that the effect of one independent variable does depend on the level of the other independent variable. In our example:

Null Hypothesis: The effect of gender does not depend on the type of shampoo.

Research Hypothesis: The effect of gender depends on the type of shampoo.

Step 3. Determine the characteristics of the comparison distribution.

For our two-way ANOVA, we need to provide degrees of freedom for each of the three comparison distributions. There will be two sets of degrees of freedom for our main effects and one for our interaction. Each of our three F statistics will be a ratio between the between-groups variance and within-groups variance. We will have three between-groups variance estimates for each of our three effects, and each one will have separate degrees of freedom. Our within-groups estimate is the same for all three.

The between-groups degrees of freedom for the two-way ANOVA for both of our main effects are the same as for a one-way ANOVA. It is just the number of groups minus 1. In our example, there were two groups for gender so: $df_{rows(gender)} = N_{rows} - 1 = 2 - 1 = 1$. There were also two groups for product type so: $df_{columns(product\ type)} = N_{columns} - 1 = 2 - 1 = 1$. For the between-groups degrees of freedom for *the interaction, we multiply the degrees of freedom for the two main effects so:* $df_{interaction} = (df_{rows(gender)})(df_{columns(product\ type)}) = (1)(1)$.

We calculate the between-groups degrees of freedom in the same way as we did for a one-way ANOVA. Specifically, we calculate the sum of the degrees of freedom in each cell. If you recall, there are four testers in each of cell, so $4 - 1 = 3$. Then, there are four cells for each of our groups: $3 + 3 + 3 + 3 = 12$. Therefore, $df_{within} = 12$.

If we calculate the total degrees of freedom, we will be able to do a quick check of our work. The total degrees of freedom are the same in a two-way ANOVA as a one-way—the total number of participants minus 1. We had 12 product testers in total so our total degrees of freedom equal 11. If we add up our three between-groups degrees of freedom (the two for the main effect and the one for the interaction) and the within-groups degrees of freedom, they should equal the total degrees of freedom. For our example, $1 + 1 + 1 + 12 = 15$.

Step 4. Determine critical values, or cutoffs.

There are three critical values or cutoffs, for each of the F ratios. We'll determine our critical values the same way that we did for a one-way ANOVA using Appendix B of your text. We look up the within-groups degrees of freedom on the left-hand side of the table (which is the same for all of our main effects and our interaction) and then look up our between-groups degrees of freedom across the top. The spot on the grid where they intersect will contain three numbers for our significance level. Generally, we want the significance level at 0.05; however, if we choose 0.01 or 0.10 we can find that there as well.

Using our example, our within-groups degrees of freedom was 12 and each of our between-groups degrees of freedom was 1. If we want a p level of 0.05, our cutoff is 4.75. If any of our obtained F ratios exceeds 4.75 for our main effects and/or the interaction, we will be able to reject the associated null hypothesis.

Step 5. Calculate the test statistic.

If you remember for our one-way ANOVA, we needed to calculate one F statistic. As you may have already guessed, for a two-way ANOVA we'll need to calculate three F statistics—one for each main effect and one for the interaction.

Our first step is to calculate the total sum of squares. The formula for the total sum of squares is: $SS_{total} = \ (X - GM)^2$. Just as we did for our one-way ANOVA, this means that we subtract the grand mean (the overall mean of our entire sample) from every score, square the deviation, and add up all of the deviations. You may remember that when we first introduced the data, the grand mean (GM) was 6.75. This process is elaborated in the following table:

	Liking ratings for each participant in each group (X)	Subtract grand mean from each score ($X - GM$)	Square the deviations, $(X - GM)^2$
Female, Best-Seller	5	$(5 - 6.75) = -1.75$	3.06
	5	$(5 - 6.75) = -1.75$	3.06
	6	$(6 - 6.75) = -0.75$	0.56
	6	$(6 - 6.75) = -0.75$	0.56
Female, New Product	9	$(9 - 6.75) = 2.25$	5.06
	9	$(9 - 6.75) = 2.25$	5.06
	9	$(9 - 6.75) = 2.25$	5.06
	10	$(10 - 6.75) = 3.25$	10.56
Male, Best-Seller	4	$(4 - 6.75) = -2.75$	7.56
	5	$(5 - 6.75) = -1.75$	3.06
	6	$(6 - 6.75) = -0.75$	0.56
	8	$(8 - 6.75) = 1.25$	1.56
Male, New Product	6	$(6 - 6.75) = -0.75$	0.56
	6	$(6 - 6.75) = -0.75$	0.56
	7	$(7 - 6.75) = 0.25$	0.06
	7	$(7 - 6.75) = 0.25$	0.06
			Total Sum of Squares (SS_{total}) = 46.96

Next, let's work on the between-groups sum of squares for our main effects. This is not different from the between-groups sum of squares for the one-way ANOVA. The difference is that now we need to do two of them. We'll start with calculating the sum of squares for gender. We calculate this by subtracting the grand mean from the mean for each level of gender for each score.

	Liking ratings for each participant in each group (X)	Mean for gender level, $M_{row(gender)}$	Subtract grand mean from mean for each level of the variable ($M_{row(gender)} - GM$)	Square the deviations, ($M_{row(gender)} - GM$)^2
Female, Best-Seller	5 5 6 6		(7.38 − 6.75) = 0.63 (7.38 − 6.75) = 0.63 (7.38 − 6.75) = 0.63 (7.38 − 6.75) = 0.63	0.40 0.40 0.40 0.40
Female, New Product	9 9 9 10	7.38	(7.38 − 6.75) = 0.63 (7.38 − 6.75) = 0.63 (7.38 − 6.75) = 0.63 (7.38 − 6.75) = 0.63	0.40 0.40 0.40 0.40
Male, Best Seller	4 5 6 8		(6.13 − 6.75) = −0.62 (6.13 − 6.75) = −0.62 (6.13 − 6.75) = −0.62 (6.13 − 6.75) = −0.62	0.38 0.38 0.38 0.38
Male, New Product	6 6 7 7	6.13	(6.13 − 6.75) = −0.62 (6.13 − 6.75) = −0.62 (6.13 − 6.75) = −0.62 (6.13 − 6.75) = −0.62	0.38 0.38 0.38 0.38
				Sum of Squares for Gender ($SS_{row\,(gender)}$) = **6.24**

We'll do the same thing for our column variable—product type. The table has been slightly rearranged to make it easier to read.

	Liking ratings for each participant in each group (X)	Mean for product type level, $M_{column(product)}$	Subtract grand mean from mean for each level of the variable $(M_{column(product)} - GM)$	Square the deviations, $(M_{column(product)} - GM)^2$
Female, Best-Seller	5 5 6 6		$(5.63 - 6.75) = -1.12$ $(5.63 - 6.75) = -1.12$ $(5.63 - 6.75) = -1.12$ $(5.63 - 6.75) = -1.12$	1.25 1.25 1.25 1.25
Male, Best-Seller	4 5 6 8	5.63	$(5.63 - 6.75) = -1.12$ $(5.63 - 6.75) = -1.12$ $(5.63 - 6.75) = -1.12$ $(5.63 - 6.75) = -1.12$	1.25 1.25 1.25 1.25
Female, New Product	9 9 9 10		$(7.88 - 6.75) = 1.13$ $(7.88 - 6.75) = 1.13$ $(7.88 - 6.75) = 1.13$ $(7.88 - 6.75) = 1.13$	1.28 1.28 1.28 1.28
Male, New Product	6 6 7 7	7.88	$(7.88 - 6.75) = 1.13$ $(7.88 - 6.75) = 1.13$ $(7.88 - 6.75) = 1.13$ $(7.88 - 6.75) = 1.13$	1.28 1.28 1.28 1.28
				Sum of Squares for Product $(SS_{column\,(product)}) = 20.24$

Our next step is to calculate the within-groups sum of squares, which is the same as what we did for the one-way ANOVA. For each of our 16 scores, we will subtract the cell mean from that individual score, then square and sum the deviations. This has been elaborated in the following table:

	Liking ratings for each participant in each group (X)	Cell Mean (M_{cell})	Subtract grand mean from each score ($X - M_{cell}$)	Square the deviations ($X - M_{cell})^2$
Female, Best-Seller	5 5 6 6	5.50	$(5 - 5.50) = -0.5$ $(5 - 5.50) = -0.5$ $(6 - 5.50) = 0.5$ $(6 - 5.50) = 0.5$	0.25 0.25 0.25 0.25
Female, New Product	9 9 9 10	9.25	$(9 - 9.25) = -0.25$ $(9 - 9.25) = -0.25$ $(9 - 9.25) = -0.25$ $(10 - 9.25) = 0.75$	0.063 0.063 0.063 0.56
Male, Best Seller	4 5 6 8	5.75	$(4 - 5.75) = -1.75$ $(5 - 5.75) = -0.75$ $(6 - 5.75) = 0.25$ $(8 - 5.75) = 2.25$	3.06 0.56 0.063 5.06
Male, New Product	6 6 7 7	6.50	$(6 - 6.50) = -0.5$ $(6 - 6.50) = -0.5$ $(7 - 6.50) = 0.5$ $(7 - 6.50) = 0.5$	0.25 0.25 0.25 0.25
				Sum of Squares Within (SS_{within}) **= 11.49**

We now just have one more sum of squares to calculate—that for the interaction. The simplest way to find this is to remember that the total sum of squares is the sum of the sum of squares for our main effects, the interaction, and within. In other words, $SS_{interaction} = SS_{total} - (SS_{rows} + SS_{columns} + SS_{within})$. For our example, we can calculate this by: $SS_{interaction} = SS_{total} - (SS_{gender} + SS_{product} + SS_{within})$ or $SS_{interaction} = 46.96 - (6.24 + 20.24 + 11.49) = 46.96 - (37.97) = 8.99$.

With this information, we can go ahead and put together our source table with all of the various pieces of our puzzle. Remember that to calculate the mean squares for each piece, we'll need to divide each sum of squares by its corresponding degrees of freedom. Each of our F statistics is calculated in the same way as with the one-way ANOVA, that is, by dividing the mean square between by the mean square within (see formulas in Table 12-18 on page 328 of the text).

Source	SS	Df	MS	F
Gender	6.24	1	6.24	6.50
Product	20.24	1	20.24	21.08
Gender × Product	8.99	1	8.99	9.36
Within	11.49	12	0.96	
Total	46.96	15		

Step 6. Make a decision.

As previously mentioned, if any of our test statistics exceeds 4.75, we can reject the null hypothesis. If we can reject the null hypothesis for our interaction, we will want to draw the pattern of our data on a graph which will allow us to interpret our data. If we have more than two levels in any of our groups, we will want to conduct post-hoc tests. In general, we will also focus on the interaction rather than on any significant main effects. However, if the interaction is not statistically significant, we will focus our attention on our main effects.

In our example, all three *F* statistics exceed 4.75. As a result, we can conclude that the interaction effect is significant as well as both of our main effects. At this point, it is a good idea to graph our findings to visualize what exactly is going on. We can also draw lines to confirm that there is an interaction. If we extend the lines, we would see that the lines intersect.

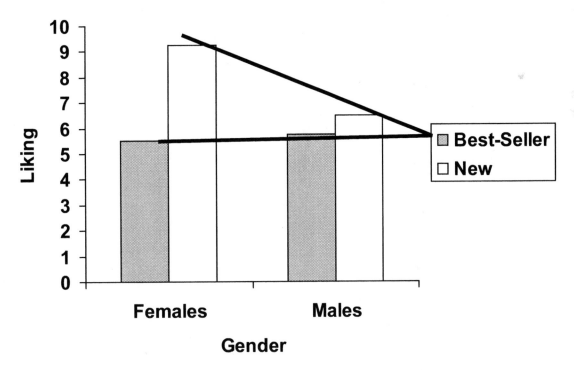

Now that we've done our analyses and confirmed the presence of our interaction through a graph, we can go ahead and interpret the data. So, do our raters prefer the new shampoo and should we market this to men or women? Our main effect for product tells us that overall, our raters did prefer the new product compared to the best-seller. However, this doesn't tell us the whole story. If we look closely at our interaction, female testers especially liked the new product. As a result, we'd be wise to market the new product to women in particular if we want to sell the most shampoo!

Effect Size for Two-Way ANOVA

Now we calculate the effect size for each main effect and the interaction, with a modification to the formula we have been using.

$$R^2_{gender} = \frac{SS_{gender}}{\left(SS_{total} - SS_{product} - SS_{gender \times product}\right)} = \frac{6.24}{(46.96 - 20.24 - 8.99)} = 0.352$$

$$R^2_{product} = \frac{SS_{product}}{\left(SS_{total} - SS_{gender} - SS_{gender \times product}\right)} = \frac{20.24}{(46.96 - 6.24 - 8.99)} = 0.638$$

$$R^2_{gender \times product} = \frac{SS_{gender \times product}}{\left(SS_{total} - SS_{gender} - SS_{product}\right)} = \frac{8.99}{(46.96 - 6.24 - 20.24)} = 0.439$$

According to the conventions presented in Table 12-20 in the text, these effect sizes are all large.

STUDY QUESTIONS

1. A **two-way** ANOVA includes:
   a. one independent variable with at least two levels.
   b. one independent variable with no more than two levels.
   c. two independent variables.
   d. two dependent variables.

2. A study comparing freshmen, sophomores, juniors, and seniors on some dependent measure:
   a. has four independent variables.
   b. would be termed a four-way factorial ANOVA.
   c. is a two-way ANOVA, with two levels of each independent variable.
   d. has one independent variable with four levels.

3. The term **mixed-design ANOVA** refers to a factorial design that includes:
   a. at least one manipulated factor and at lease one nonmanipulated factor.
   b. one or more between-groups factors and one or more within-groups factors.
   c. one or more nominal independent variables and one or more interval independent variables.
   d. at least one qualitative interaction and at least one quantitative interaction.

4. A **factorial analysis of variance:**
   a. includes at least one nominal independent variable.
   b. includes at least three levels of each independent variable in the analysis.
   c. examines the effects of two or more independent variables in one study.
   d. uses factor analysis to examine the effect of an experimental manipulation.

5. The advantage of a two-way ANOVA over conducting separate one-way ANOVAs is that it allows the researcher to:
   a. study more variables using fewer participants.
   b. study the effects of combining two or more variables.
   c. save money by assigning participants to more than one group.
   d. combine independent and dependent variables in one experiment.

6. Each unique combination of levels of the factors in a factorial design is called a(n):
   a. marginal mean.
   b. interaction.
   c. cell.
   d. factor.

7. The following shows the design of the Langer, Blank, and Chanowitz (1978) field experiment:

Information Accompanying Request

		No Information	Placebic Information	Real Information
Size of Request	Small (5 copies)	$n = 15$	$n = 15$	$n = 16$
	Large (20 Copies)	$n = 25$	$n = 25$	$n = 24$

The statistical procedure used to analyze the results of this study is most accurately described as a:
   a. one-way between-groups ANOVA.
   b. one-way within-groups ANOVA.
   c. 3 × 2 between-groups ANOVA.
   d. 3 × 2 within-groups ANOVA.

8. Niedenthal and Setterlund (1994) used a factorial design to study the effects of word type (*happy, positive, neutral, negative,* and *sad*) and mood (*happy, sad*) on decision latencies in a lexical decision task. How many cells are in this design?
   a. 2
   b. 5
   c. 7
   d. 10

9. A **main effect** is observed when:
   a. one of the independent variables has an influence on the dependent variable.
   b. the effect of one variable is much greater than the effect(s) of the other variable(s).
   c. at least one cell mean is significantly different from at least one other cell mean.
   d. there is no interaction effect.

10. An **interaction** occurs when:
   a. the independent variables influence each other but not the dependent variable.
   b. only one independent variable has an effect on the dependent variable.
   c. the effect of one variable depends on the level of another variable.
   d. both independent variables affect the dependent variable.

11. How many main and interaction effects are possible in a 2 × 3 factorial ANOVA?
   a. 2 main effects and 1 interaction effect
   b. 2 main effects and 3 interaction effects
   c. 3 main effects and 2 interaction effects
   d. 6 main effects and 2 interaction effects

12. Consider the following table of means:

Factor A

		A1	A2	
Factor B	**B1**	50	80	65
	B2	80	50	65
		65	65	

The table shows that the effect of Factor *A* reverses direction across the levels of Factor *B*. This pattern would be most specifically described as a:
a. main effect of Factor *A*, but no main effect of Factor *B*.
b. main effect of Factor *B*, but no main effect of Factor *A*.
c. quantitative interaction effect.
d. qualitative interaction effect.

13. Consider the following table of means:

Factor A

		A1	A2	
Factor B	**B1**	50	50	50
	B2	80	80	80
		65	65	

The row and column means are:
a. used to identify the presence of a quantitative interaction.
b. used to identify the presence of a qualitative interaction.
c. called marginal means.
d. called cell means.

14. Consider the following table of means:

		A1	A2	
Factor B	**B1**	50	50	50
	B2	80	80	80
		65	65	

The mean of level *B1* (50) differs substantially from the mean of level *B2* (80), indicating a(n):
a. main effect of Factor *A*.
b. main effect of Factor *B*.
c. interaction between the levels of Factor *A*.
d. interaction between the levels of Factor *B*.

15. Consider the following table of means:

Factor A

		A1	A2	
Factor B	B1	40	60	50
	B2	60	80	70
		50	70	

Notice that the mean of level $A1$ (50) differs substantially from the mean of level $A2$ (70), just as the mean of level $B1$ (50) is substantially different from the mean of level $B2$ (70). Notice also that the increase in the levels of Factor A across level $B1$ (from 40 to 60) is the same as the increase in the levels of Factor A across level $B2$ (from 60 to 80). This pattern of means indicates:

a. the main effects of Factors A and B but no interaction.
b. the main effects of Factors A and B and an interaction.
c. a quantitative interaction but no main effects.
d. a qualitative interaction but no main effects.

16. Consider the following table of means:

Factor A

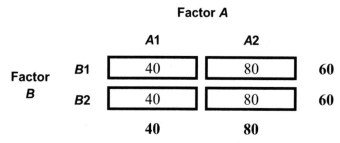

		A1	A2	
Factor B	B1	40	80	60
	B2	40	80	60
		40	80	

Notice that the mean of level $A1$ (40) differs substantially from the mean of level $A2$ (80), but the mean of level $B1$ (60) is the same as the mean of level $B2$ (60). Notice also that the increase in the levels of Factor A across level $B1$ (from 40 to 80) is the same as the increase in the levels of Factor A across level $B2$ (from 40 to 80). This pattern of means indicates:

a. the main effects of Factors A and B but no interaction.
b. the main effects of Factors A and B and an interaction.
c. a main effect of Factor A, but no other effects.
d. an interaction, but no other effects.

17. Consider the following table of means:

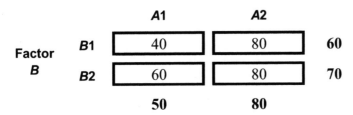

Factor A

		A1	A2	
Factor B	**B1**	40	80	60
	B2	60	80	70
		50	80	

Notice that the mean of level *A*1 (50) differs substantially from the mean of level *A*2 (80), and the mean of level *B*1 (60) differs quite a bit from the mean of level *B*2 (70). Notice also that the increase in the levels of Factor *A* across level *B*1 (from 40 to 80) is not the same as the increase in the levels of Factor *A* across level *B*2 (from 60 to 80). This pattern of means indicates:
 a. the main effects of Factors *A* and *B* but no interaction.
 b. the main effects of Factors *A* and *B* and an interaction.
 c. a main effect of Factor *A*, but no other effects.
 d. a main effect of Factor *B*, but no other effects.

18. You should inspect the _____ means to determine whether there is likely to be an interaction in a two-way ANOVA.
 a. row
 b. column
 c. pattern of cell
 d. row and column

19. The following figure displays a hypothetical result of a study in which students read a brief description of a woman before they use a scale to rate the likelihood that the woman would be sexually harassed. The independent variables were the gender of the student rater and the length of the woman's hair ("short" vs. "mid-length" vs. "long").

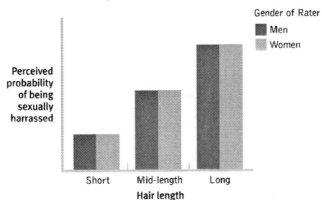

Identify the effect(s) displayed in the figure.
 a. There is a main effect of gender but no other effects.
 b. There is a main effect of hair length but no other effects.
 c. There is a main effect of hair length and an interaction.
 d. There are no main effects and no interaction.

20. The following figure displays a hypothetical result of a study in which students read a brief description of a woman before they use a scale to rate the likelihood that the woman would be sexually harassed. The independent variables were the gender of the student rater and the length of the woman's hair ("short" vs. "mid-length" vs. "long").

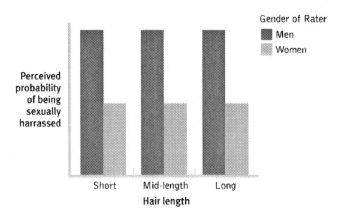

Identify the effect(s) displayed in the figure.
a. There is a main effect of hair length but no other effects.
b. There is a main effect of gender but no other effects.
c. There are main effects of both gender and hair length but no interaction.
d. There is an interaction but no main effects.

21. The following figure displays a hypothetical result of a study in which students read a brief description of a woman before they use a scale to rate the likelihood that the woman would be sexually harassed. The independent variables were the gender of the student rater and the length of the woman's hair ("short" vs. "mid-length" vs. "long").

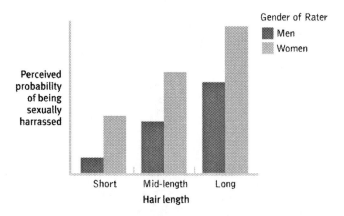

Identify the effect(s) displayed in the figure.
a. There is a main effect of gender but no other effects.
b. There is a main effect of hair length but no other effects.
c. There are main effects of both gender and hair length but no interaction.
d. There is an interaction but no main effects.

22. The following figure displays a hypothetical result of a study in which students read a brief description of a woman before they use a scale to rate the likelihood that the woman would be sexually harassed. The independent variables were the gender of the student rater and the length of the woman's hair ("short" vs. "mid-length" vs. "long").

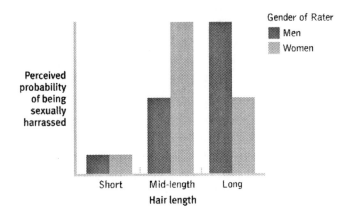

Identify the effect(s) displayed in the figure.
a. There is a main effect of gender but no other effects.
b. There is a main effect of hair length but no other effects.
c. There are main effects of both gender and hair length but no interaction.
d. There is an interaction but no main effects.

23. The following figure displays a hypothetical result of a study in which students read a brief description of a woman before they use a scale to rate the likelihood that the woman would be sexually harassed. The independent variables were the gender of the student rater and the length of the woman's hair ("short" vs. "mid-length" vs. "long").

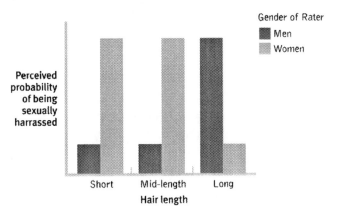

Identify the effect(s) displayed in the figure.
a. There is a main effect of gender and an interaction.
b. There is a main effect of hair length and an interaction.
c. There are main effects of both gender and hair length but no interaction.
d. There is an interaction but no main effects.

Refer to the following study description to answer the next two review questions.

Study Description. In a study by Lambert, Khan, Lickel, and Fricke (1997), participants were asked to play the role of a job interviewer and form a preliminary evaluation of the fitness of a job applicant for the position of flight attendant. More specifically, each participant read a description of the job followed by a vita of the applicant that included personal information as well as a prominently displayed black and white photograph of an attractive woman in her twenties. After reading the job description and the vita, each participant used a 10-point scale to rate the likelihood that he or she would hire the applicant. Half of the participants rated the applicant after being asked to imagine a personal episode of their lives that made them feel very sad whenever they thought of it and half rated the applicant in a mood-neutral condition. In addition, half of the participants in each mood condition (sad versus neutral) rated the applicant based on a job description that emphasized customer relations and the positive role of physical attractiveness in passenger satisfaction (stereotype-appropriate condition), while the other half made their ratings based on a job description that emphasized rational and analytical problem-solving skills (stereotype-inappropriate condition).

24. Refer to the **Study Description**.

Mood

	Sad	Neutral	
Stereotype-Appropriate	8.4	6.8	**7.6**
Stereotype-Inappropriate	6.4	4.6	**5.5**
	7.4	**5.7**	

Job Description (row label)

The table of means shows that sad participants were more willing to hire the applicant than mood-neutral participants, and participants who read the job description that valued physical attractiveness (the stereotype-appropriate job description) were also more willing to hire the applicant than participants who read the job description that valued analytical, problem-solving skills (the stereotype-inappropriate job description). However, these effects do not influence each other; that is, the effect of being sad on the likelihood-of-hiring ratings is not altered by the appropriateness of the stereotype for the job description and vice versa. This is an example of:

a. a main effect of mood but no other effects.
b. a main effect of job description but no other effects.
c. main effects of mood and job description but no interaction.
d. an interaction between mood and job description but with no main effects.

25. Refer to the **Study Description**.

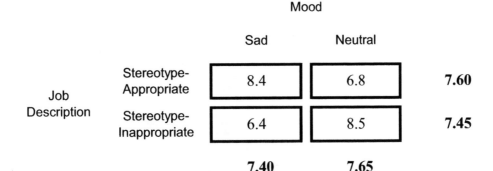

The table of means shows that sad participants were less likely to hire the applicant when the stereotype was inappropriate (the job description valued analytical problem-solving skills), whereas the participants in a neutral mood were more likely to hire the applicant when the stereotype was inappropriate. This is an example of:

a. a qualitative interaction but no main effects.
b. a quantitative interaction but no main effects.
c. two main effects but no interaction.
d. the effects of the factors canceling each other, so there are no effects of any kind.

26. In a two-factor ANOVA, there is (are) _____ hypothesis(es) to be tested.

a. one
b. two
c. three
d. The number of hypotheses depends on the number of levels of each factor.

27. The following table shows the number of participants in each cell of the 3 × 2 factorial design used by Langer et al. (1978):

Information Accompanying Request

		No Information	Placebic Information	Real Information
Size of Request	Small (5 copies)	$n = 15$	$n = 15$	$n = 16$
	Large (20 Copies)	$n = 25$	$n = 25$	$n = 24$

Which one of the following is the correct method of determining, and the correct number of, degrees of freedom for the effect of the information (column) factor?

a. number of cells – number of columns = 6 – 3 = 3
b. (number of columns – 1) (number of rows – 1) = (2) (1) = 2
c. number of cells – 1 = 6 – 1 = 5
d. number of columns – 1 = 3 – 1 = 2

28. The following table shows the number of participants in each cell of the 3×2 factorial design used by Langer et al. (1978):

Information Accompanying Request

		No Information	Placebic Information	Real Information
Size of Request	Small (5 copies)	$n = 15$	$n = 15$	$n = 16$
	Large (20 Copies)	$n = 25$	$n = 25$	$n = 24$

Which one of the following is the correct method of determining, and the correct number of, degrees of freedom for the information × request interaction?
a. number of cells – number of columns = 6 – 3 = 3
b. (number of columns – 1) (number of rows – 1) = (2) (1) = 2
c. number of cells – 1 = 6 – 1 = 5
d. number of columns – 1 = 3 – 1 = 2

29. The following table shows the number of participants in each cell of the 3×2 factorial design used by Langer et al. (1978):

Information Accompanying Request

		No Information	Placebic Information	Real Information
Size of Request	Small (5 copies)	$n = 15$	$n = 15$	$n = 16$
	Large (20 Copies)	$n = 25$	$n = 25$	$n = 24$

Which one of the following is the correct method of determining, and the correct number of, the within-groups degrees of freedom?
a. Find the cell with the smallest number of participants and multiply this value by the number of cells: (15) (6) = 90.
b. Subtract 1 from the number of participants in each cell and sum: 14 + 14 + 15 + 24 + 24 + 23 = 114.
c. Average the number of participants in each cell: (15 + 15 + 16 + 25 + 25 + 24) / 6 = 120 / 6 = 20.
d. Sum the number of participants in the cells and subtract 1: 120 – 1 = 119.

30. How many sources of variability are in a two-way ANOVA?
    a. four
    b. three
    c. two
    d. The number varies, depending on the number of levels of each factor.

31. Analysis of Variance Source Table for the Langer et al. (1978) Study:

Source	SS	df	MS	F	p
Information	1.288	2	0.644	3.593	0.031
Request	7.805	1	7.805	43.563	0.000
Information X Request	0.521	2	0.261	1.454	0.238
Error	20.424	114	0.179		
Total	60.000	120			

Refer to the previous table. Which of the following describes the results?
a. There are two main effects and an interaction.
b. There are two main effects.
c. There is one main effect.
d. There is an interaction.

32. Effect size for the two-way ANOVA is calculated using R^2. For a 3 × 4 ANOVA, where the factors are age group (three levels) and geographic region (four levels), how many effect size computations will need to be performed?
a. 2, one for each main effect, age and region
b. 1 for the interaction
c. 3, one for each main effect, age and region, and one for the interaction
d. 4, one for each main effect, age and region, one for the interaction, and one for the dependent variable

ANSWERS TO CHAPTER 12 STUDY QUESTIONS

Question Number	Correct Answer
1	c, p. 305
2	d, p. 305
3	b, p. 305
4	c, p. 305
5	b, p. 306
6	c, p. 307
7	c, p. 307
8	d, p. 307
9	a, p. 307
10	c, pp. 308–311
11	a, p. 308
12	d, p. 311
13	c, p. 312
14	b, p. 312
15	a, pp. 312–313
16	c, pp. 312–313
17	b, pp. 312–313

Question Number	Correct Answer
18	c, p. 312
19	b, pp. 312–317
20	b, pp. 312–317
21	c, pp. 312–317
22	d, pp. 312–317
23	a, pp. 312–317
24	c (review of main and interaction effects), pp. 309–317
25	a (review of main and interaction effects), pp. 309–317
26	c, p. 321
27	d, pp. 322–323
28	b, pp. 322–323
29	b, pp. 322–323
30	a, pp. 324–328
31	b, p. 328
32	c, p. 329

CHAPTER THIRTEEN

Correlation

CHAPTER OUTLINE

Correlation
- The Characteristics of Correlation
- Correlation is Not Causation

The Pearson Correlation Coefficient
- Calculation of the Pearson Correlation Coefficient
- Hypothesis Testing with the Pearson Correlation Coefficient

LEARNING OBJECTIVES

After studying this chapter, you should be able to:

1. Define each of the following terms and provide examples that are not in the text: *correlation coefficient, positive correlation, negative correlation, scatterplot, Pearson correlation coefficient.*

2. Discuss the limits of a correlation coefficient as it may be used to describe the relation between two variables, including inferences about causal relations.

3. Demonstrate facility with the calculation and application of the Pearson correlation coefficient for hypothesis testing.

CHAPTER REVIEW

> **Correlation**

The Characteristics of Correlation

A **correlation coefficient** is a precise quantitative measure of the strength and direction of a linear association between two variables, both of which are usually measured on an interval scale. A linear relation between two variables is disclosed in a scatterplot like the one on the next page. Each point in a scatterplot represents the intersection of a single participant's scores on each of two variables. Note that the pattern of points may be approximated by the broken line that slopes upward from left to right.

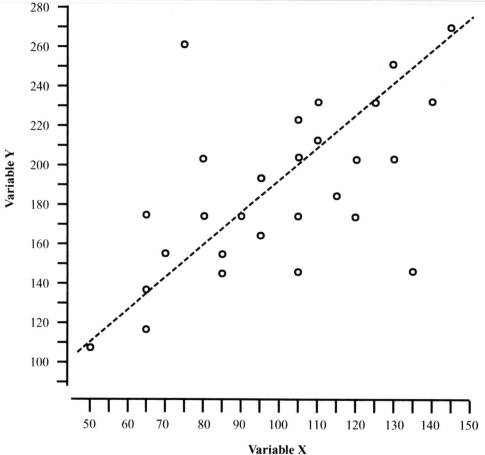

The *sign* of the correlation coefficient indicates the *direction* of the linear relation. The scatterplot above depicts a **positive correlation**. Two variables are positively correlated when participants with high scores on one variable tend to have high scores on the other variable (and those with medium and low scores on one variable tend to have medium and low scores, respectively, on the second variable). In contrast, a **negative** (also called an *inverse*) **correlation** is one in which higher scores on one variable are associated with lower scores on the other variable. A scatterplot displaying a negative linear relation is like a mirror image of a scatterplot showing a positive correlation.

The range of possible values of a correlation coefficient is −1 to 1. The values −1 and 1 represent perfect correlations which, in turn, reflect perfect linear relations between variables. A perfect linear relation is one in which all of the points in a scatterplot fall along a straight line that has either a positive or negative slope. As noted in the text, correlations of exactly ±1 or 0 are almost never encountered in the "real world," and there are no perfect correlations between variables studied in the social and behavioral sciences. However, you can imagine a class in which the grade is determined only by attendance; there are 25 classes and each one attended adds 4 points to the grade. As long as there is at least some variability in class attendance, the correlation between class attendance and final grade will be 1.

The *magnitude*, or absolute value, of the correlation coefficient is a precise measure of the *strength* of the linear relation: the closer the correlation coefficient to 1, the stronger the linear relation between the variables, *irrespective of the sign of the coefficient.* Don't miss the point that the strength of a linear relation is completely independent of the direction of that relation. For example, a correlation of –0.46 indicates a stronger linear relation than a correlation of 0.37.

The strength of a linear association may also be estimated from the pattern of points in a scatterplot. The greater the strength of the relation, the smaller the average vertical distance between the points and a line drawn to fit them. Conversely, the greater the average vertical distance between the points and the line, the weaker the linear relation between the variables. To illustrate these points, lines were drawn to fit the patterns of data in each of the scatterplots below. The correlation coefficient computed for the scatterplot on the left is –0.45; for the scatterplot on the right, the correlation coefficient is –0.94.

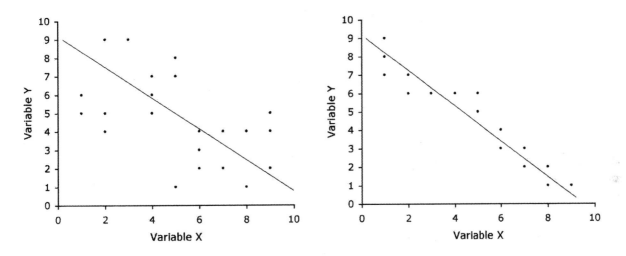

Of the linear relations displayed above, which one do you suppose to be more common in the behavioral and social sciences? If you said the one on the left, then you are correct. Correlations between variables studied in the social and behavioral sciences typically do not exceed 0.4 in absolute value. As noted in the text, Cohen (1988) reported that a correlation considered "large" by social science standards must be at least 0.5; a correlation of "medium" or "moderate" size is around 0.3; and a "small" correlation is near 0.1.

If the correlation coefficient is close to zero, then there is essentially no *linear* relation between the two variables; the variables may be related, but that relation cannot be linear.

Correlation Is Not Causation

A correlation between variables does not mean that the variables are causally related. If an increase in the values of one variable causes an increase (or a decrease) in the values of a second variable, then the variables are strongly correlated, but it does not follow that strongly correlated variables are causally related. Why not? It may be that strongly correlated variables are not causally related to each other, but are both causally related to a third variable. In short, a correlation between two variables, *A* and *B*, may result from any of the following:

1. Changes in the values of Variable *A* cause changes in the values of Variable *B*.
2. Changes in the values of Variable *B* cause changes in the values of Variable *A*.
3. Changes in the values of Variables *A* and *B* are caused by changes in Variable *C*.

The point is that correlation alone does not disclose which of these alternatives is correct. Consider the following problem. For a large sample of middle-aged men, the correlation between income and blood pressure is 0.74. Does this mean that men with higher incomes tend to have jobs that involve greater responsibility, and this greater responsibility causes stress that manifests as higher blood pressure? If you agree with this interpretation, then you've just endorsed the idea that a correlation between two variables means that changes in one variable cause changes in the other. You've agreed that the relatively high correlation between income and blood pressure is evidence of a causal chain: an increase in job responsibilities causes stress, and one sign of increased stress is an increase in blood pressure. This interpretation is reasonable, but only as an alternative among several. A more parsimonious interpretation is that the correlation between income and blood pressure is a product of aging. As men age, their incomes increase as does their blood pressure. More specifically, income increases with experience, and it is impossible to acquire experience apart from aging. An increase in blood pressure is a result of physical changes associated with aging. The correlation between Variable *A* (income) and Variable *B* (blood pressure) is probably caused by Variable *C* (age). Again, the correlation may be explained by any of a number of interpretations, but the correlation, alone, does not enable a determination of which of them is correct. Interpreting a correlation to be evidence of causation is arguably the most prevalent misrepresentation of a correlation coefficient.

> The Pearson Correlation Coefficient

At best, correlational studies can only disclose that variables are related; they can not reveal a direction of causality or even whether there is a direct causal link between the variables. However, for many important research questions, ethical and practical considerations limit the work of scientists to an investigation of correlation. For this reason, it is important to understand how the most frequently reported correlation coefficient, the *Pearson product-moment correlation coefficient* is computed, what it means, and what it does not mean.

In this chapter, we learn to compute the **Pearson correlation coefficient**. The symbol for the correlation coefficient is a lowercase "r" (for regression, the subject of the next chapter), so the formula will be expressed as a solution for r.

Calculation of the Pearson Correlation Coefficient

The first step in considering the relation between variables is to create a visual display, and a scatterplot is a useful depiction. We will create a scatterplot for each of the fictional data sets that follow.

Data Set 1		
Case	Variable X	Variable Y
1	6	5
2	4	4
3	3	3
4	1	2
5	1	1

Data Set 2		
Case	Variable X	Variable Y
1	6	1
2	4	2
3	3	3
4	1	4
5	1	5

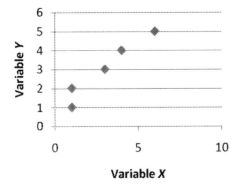

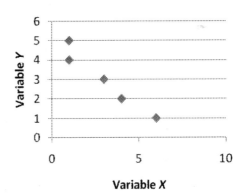

Now we compute the correlation coefficient for each of these data sets one at a time so that we can keep our numbers organized.

Data Set 1

First we compute the numerator:

Case	Variable X	$(X - M_X)$	Variable Y	$(Y - M_Y)$	$(X - M_X)(Y - M_Y)$
1	6	3	5	2	6
2	4	1	4	1	1
3	3	0	3	0	0
4	1	−2	1	−2	4
5	1	−2	2	−1	2
	$M_X = 3$		$M_Y = 3$		$\Sigma(X - M_X)(Y - M_Y) = 13$

Then we compute the denominator:

Case	Variable X	$(X - M_X)$	$(X - M_X)^2$	Variable Y	$(Y - M_Y)$	$(Y - M_Y)^2$
1	6	3	9	5	2	4
2	4	1	1	4	1	1
3	3	0	0	3	0	0
4	1	−2	4	1	−2	4
	1	−2	4	2	−1	1
			$\Sigma(X - M_X)^2 = 18$			$\Sigma(Y - M_Y)^2 = 10$

Now we can compute the correlation coefficient.

$$r = \frac{\Sigma(X - M_X)(Y - M_Y)}{\sqrt{(SS_X)(SS_Y)}} = \frac{13}{\sqrt{(18)(10)}} = \frac{13}{13.416} = 0.969$$

The Pearson correlation for these data, r, is 0.969, which is a very strong positive correlation.

For the second set of data, the only thing that changes is the numerator. Here are all the calculations so that you can get some practice.

Case	Variable X	$(X - M_X)$	Variable Y	$(Y - M_Y)$	$(X - M_X)(Y - M_Y)$
1	6	3	1	−2	−6
2	4	1	2	−1	−1
3	3	0	3	0	0
4	1	−2	4	1	−2
5	1	−2	5	2	−4
	$M_X = 3$		$M_Y = 3$		$\Sigma(X - M_X)(Y - M_Y) = -13$

Case	Variable X	$(X - M_X)$	$(X - M_X)^2$	Variable Y	$(Y - M_Y)$	$(Y - M_Y)^2$
1	6	3	9	1	−2	4
2	4	1	1	2	−1	1
3	3	0	0	3	0	0
4	1	−2	4	4	1	1
5	1	−2	4	5	2	4
			$\Sigma(X - M_X)^2 = 18$			$\Sigma(Y - M_Y)^2 = 10$

$$r = \frac{\Sigma(X - M_X)(Y - M_Y)}{\sqrt{(SS_X)(SS_Y)}} = \frac{-13}{\sqrt{(18)(10)}} = \frac{-13}{13.416} = -0.969$$

Again, this is a strong correlation in a negative direction.

Hypothesis Testing with the Pearson Correlation Coefficient

For this exercise, let's just consider the first data set. Imagine that variable X is number of close friends and variable Y is the number of text messages received in a day.

Step 1. Identify the population, distribution, and assumptions. The populations of interest are people who have friends and text message, whether or not there is a relation between those two variables for the people. The comparison distribution is all possible correlations of these variables, taken from this population, and based on five observations. In terms of assumptions, we do not know if our data were randomly selected, and we do not know if the underlying distributions are normal. However, we can see that each variable has an equal amount of variability, so we have met the third assumption.

Step 2. State the null and research hypotheses.

Null Hypothesis: There is no correlation between these variables, $r = 0$.

Research Hypothesis: There is a correlation, $r \neq 0$.

Step 3. Determine the characteristics of the comparison distribution. The comparison distribution is an r distribution with 3 degrees of freedom.

$$df_r = N - 2 = 5 - 2 = 3$$

Step 4. Determine the critical values, or cutoffs. The cutoffs are –0.878 and 0.878.

Step 5. Calculate the test statistic, which we found to be $r = 0.969$.

Step 6. Make a decision. Because the correlation coefficient we calculated, $r = 0.969$, exceeds the critical cutoff of 0.878, we can reject the null hypothesis and conclude that there is a significant positive correlation between the number of friends people have and the number of text messages they receive. Of course, we cannot say anything about what might be causing this relationship because we have not assessed a cause by computing a correlation.

STUDY QUESTIONS

1. A **correlation coefficient** describes the strength and direction of a _____ relation between two variables.
   a. linear
   b. nonlinear
   c. causal
   d. exponential ·

2. There is a _____ relation between two variables when the pattern of points in a scatterplot roughly resembles a straight line.
   a. positive
   b. linear
   c. curvilinear
   d. negative

3. There is a **positive correlation** between two variables when individuals with _____ scores on one variable tend to have _____ scores on the other variable.
   a. two or more; two or more
   b. high; low
   c. positive; negative
   d. high; high

4. The pattern of data points in a graph depicting the relation between scores on the scholastic aptitude test (SAT) and first-year college grade point average (GPA) tends to slope upward and to the right, indicating a _____ correlation between these variables.
   a. weak
   b. strong
   c. positive
   d. negative

5. The range of possible values for a correlation coefficient is:
   a. determined by the means and standard deviations of the two correlated variables.
   b. interpreted directly from a scatterplot depicting the relation between two variables.
   c. determined by the range of scores for the two variables.
   d. between –1 and 1.

6. There is a **negative correlation** between two variables when cases with _____ scores on one variable tend to have _____ scores on the other variable.
   a. high; high
   b. low; low
   c. high; low
   d. negative; negative

7. In a study of 174 factory workers, Bardsley and Rhodes (1996) found that workers who were most often late to work tended to be the ones who scored the lowest on job satisfaction. This is an example of a _____ correlation.
   a. near-zero
   b. curvilinear
   c. positive
   d. negative

8. A *perfect correlation*:
   a. has a value of either 1 or –1.
   b. has zero variability around the mean of both variables.
   c. exists only in theory and may not be computed for actual data.
   d. results when the mean of one variable is 1 and the mean of the other variable is –1.

9. The *strength* of the correlation between two linearly related variables is indicated by the:
   a. magnitude (absolute value) of the correlation coefficient.
   b. sign (positive or negative) of the correlation coefficient.
   c. length of the line in a scatterplot.
   d. number of points in a scatterplot.

10. Correlations that are _____ are fairly common in everyday life.
   a. greater than 1
   b. less than –1
   c. approximately 0
   d. approximately 1 or –1

11. Correlations that are considered "large" by Cohen's (1988) standards are _____ in the social sciences.
   a. fairly common
   b. fairly uncommon
   c. almost unheard of
   d. routinely reported

12. Choose the best description of the correlation displayed in the scatterplot below:

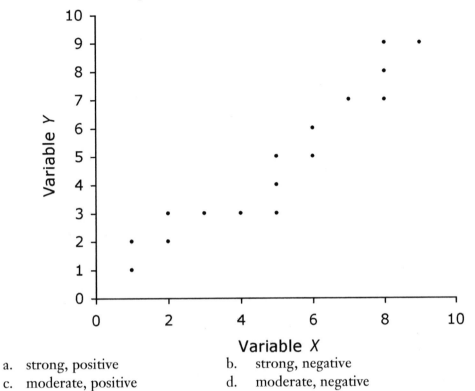

   a. strong, positive   b. strong, negative
   c. moderate, positive   d. moderate, negative

13. Choose the best description of the correlation displayed in the scatterplot below:

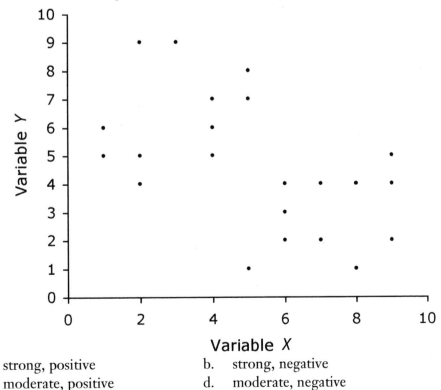

   a. strong, positive   b. strong, negative
   c. moderate, positive   d. moderate, negative

14. Which of the following variable pairs are *least* likely to be correlated?
    a. amount of time studying and amount learned
    b. the price and quality of purchased goods
    c. intelligence and physical strength
    d. shoe size and glove size

15. Which of the following is a possible explanation for a high correlation between two variables, *A* and *B*?
    a. Variable *A* causes Variable *B*, but Variable *B* does not cause Variable *A*.
    b. Variable *B* causes Variable *A*, but Variable *A* does not cause Variable *B*.
    c. A third variable causes the high correlation between Variables *A* and *B*, but Variables *A* and *B* can not be causally related.
    d. Either Variable *A* causes Variable *B*, or Variable *B* causes Variable *A*, or the correlation between Variables *A* and B is caused by a third variable.

16. The direction of causality for a correlation between two variables can only be specified if:
    a. the correlation coefficient is statistically significant.
    b. the absolute value of the correlation coefficient is greater than 0.5.
    c. a third variable that is related to both variables has been identified.
    d. False premise: A correlation can not disclose whether two variables are causally related.

17. The **Pearson correlation coefficient** quantifies a linear relation between:
    a. two nominal variables.
    b. two interval variables.
    c. two ordinal variables.
    d. two variables, at least one of which must be interval.

18. The first step in a correlational study is to:
    a. compute the correlation coefficient.
    b. construct a scatterplot.
    c. convert the raw scores to deviation scores.
    d. compute the regression coefficient.

19. In correlational research, a scatterplot is used to:
    a. quantify the relation between two variables.
    b. quantify the linear relation between two variables.
    c. confirm that the relation between two variables is roughly linear.
    d. graphically depict a causal relation between two variables.

20. Suppose that about half of the participants in a correlational study have high scores on one variable paired with high scores on the other variable (and lows paired with lows), and the remaining participants have high scores on one variable paired with low scores on the other variable (and lows paired with highs). The sum of the product deviations will be:
    a. large and positive.
    b. large and negative.
    c. approximately zero.
    d. insufficient information to answer.

21. Which one of the following tells how many standard deviations a particular individual scored above or below the mean of his or her comparison group?
    a. deviation score
    b. z score
    c. correlation coefficient
    d. standard deviation

22. A correlation is computed on 52 people, with two scores from each person. What is the critical cutoff for this hypothesis test if we ran a two-tailed test with a p level of 0.05?
    a. 0.288 and –0.288
    b. 0.273 and –0.273
    c. 0.231 and –0.231
    d. 0.263 only

23. A correlation is computed on 52 people, with two scores from each person. A correlation coefficient of –0.341 is computed on the data. What would be the result of the hypothesis test if we ran a two-tailed test with a p level of 0.05?
    a. Not enough information is provided to make a conclusion.
    b. An effect size calculation is needed before a conclusion can be made.
    c. Fail to reject the null hypothesis.
    d. Reject the null hypothesis.

ANSWERS TO CHAPTER 13 STUDY QUESTIONS

Question Number	Correct Answer
1	a, p. 343
2	b, p. 343
3	d, p. 343
4	c, p. 343
5	c, pp. 343–344
6	c, p. 344
7	d, p. 344
8	a, pp. 344–345
9	a, p. 345
10	c, pp. 345–346
11	b, p. 346
12	a, pp. 343–346
13	d, pp. 343–346

Question Number	Correct Answer
14	c, pp. 342–347
15	d, pp. 346–347
16	d, pp. 346–347 (A correlation alone can not disclose whether two variables are causally related.)
17	b, p. 348
18	b, p. 349
19	c, p. 349
20	c, p. 350
21	b, p. 351
22	b, p. 353
23	d, p. 353

CHAPTER FOURTEEN

Regression

CHAPTER OUTLINE

Simple Linear Regression
- Prediction Versus Relation
- Regression with z Scores
- Determining the Regression Equation
- The Standardized Regression Coefficient and Hypothesis Testing with Regression

Interpretation and Prediction
- Regression and Error
- Applying the Lessons of Correlation to Regression
- Regression to the Mean
- Proportionate Reduction in Error

Multiple Regression
- Understanding the Equation
- Multiple Regression in Everyday Life

LEARNING OBJECTIVES

After studying this chapter, you should be able to:

1. Define each of the following terms and provide examples that are not in the text: *simple linear regression, regression to the mean, intercept, slope, standardized regression coefficient, standard error of the estimate, proportionate reduction in error, orthogonal variable,* and *multiple regression.*
2. Describe the similarities and differences between correlation and regression.
3. Determine the regression equation and use the equation to predict values of the dependent variable for known values of the independent variable.
4. Discuss the limits of prediction using a regression equation.
5. Compute the proportionate reduction in error as a measure of effect size and relate this statistic to the correlation coefficient.
6. Distinguish between simple and multiple linear regression.

CHAPTER REVIEW

> Simple Linear Regression

Prediction versus Relation

Regression and correlation may be conceptualized as two sides of the same coin. *Correlation* focuses on the relation between variables and does not assign labels to them, whereas *regression* is more concerned with the functions of the variables in the relation and labels them accordingly. When computing a Pearson correlation coefficient, either variable may be regarded as the "*X*" or the "*Y*" variable; that is, changing the order of the variables does not change the value of the correlation coefficient. When developing a regression equation, one variable is designated as the independent (or predictor) variable, and the other as the dependent (or criterion) variable.

Think of correlation as enabling linear regression, or prediction. If two variables are correlated, then the values of one variable may be used to predict values of the second variable. **Simple linear regression** refers to the prediction of the values of the dependent variable from values of one independent variable. For example, many colleges and universities use a student's high school SAT score to predict his or her grade point average (GPA) for the first year of study. The tool used for prediction is called the *regression equation*.

Regression with z Scores

In Chapter 13, you learned to compute the correlation coefficient. In Chapter 6, you learned that the regression equation could be expressed in terms of z scores. To predict values of Variable Y, the dependent variable, from values of Variable X, the independent variable, you first converted the raw scores on both variables to z scores. Then you multiplied an individual's z score on Variable X (z_X) by the correlation coefficient (r_{XY}) to compute the predicted z score on Variable Y ($z_{\hat{Y}}$) for that individual:

$$z_{\hat{Y}} = (r_{XY})(z_X)$$

The "hat" above the subscript is used to represent a predicted value. You are using the regression equation to predict a z score on the Y variable from a z score on the X variable. Here is an example, based on real data. A certain college requires all psychology majors to take the Major Field Test (MFT) in Psychology published by the Educational Testing Service (ETS) during January of their senior year. A student who fails to score at or above the 10th percentile must pass an oral exam in order to graduate, and students who wish to graduate with honors must score at or above the 50th percentile. A senior student with a GPA of 2.32 is apprehensive about the MFT. She wonders whether her total score on the MFT will be above the minimum score (139) required for graduation. Since implementing the policy requiring senior majors to take the MFT, the Psychology Department at this institution has compiled the following statistics:

	GPA (X)	MFT (Y)
M	3.175	160.122
SD	0.492	12.977
r	0.665	

As shown in the table, the correlation between cumulative GPA and total score on the MFT in Psychology at this school is 0.665. Predict this student's total MFT score. Will she achieve the minimum total score on the MFT and avoid the oral examination?

1. Convert the student's GPA to a z score.

$$z_{GPA} = \frac{2.32 - 3.175}{0.492} = -1.738$$

2. Use the regression equation to predict this student's z score on the MFT.

$$z_{MFT} = (r_{XY})(z_{GPA}) = (0.665)(-1.738) = -1.156$$

3. Convert this student's predicted z score on the MFT to a total (scale) score on the MFT.

$$X_{MFT} = z_{MFT}(SD_{MFT}) + M_{MFT} = -1.156(12.977) + 160.122 = \textbf{145.121}$$

According to the regression equation, this student should be able to avoid the oral examination.

When using the correlation coefficient to calculate a score based on another variable, we often see **regression to the mean**. For example, the z score calculated as a predicted score will tend to be less extreme than the z score used in making the prediction. This phenomenon is discussed further later in this chapter.

Determining the Regression Equation

Now, we'll examine the steps required to predict this student's total MFT score using the regression equation. The raw-score regression equation is similar to the equation for a straight line that you learned in high school geometry: $y = mx + b$. In geometry you learned that y is a linear function of x; more specifically, y is the ordinate (or vertical axis coordinate) that you determine by multiplying x, the abscissa (or horizontal axis coordinate), by m (the slope of the line) and adding this product to b, the y-intercept, or point where the line intersects the vertical axis when x = zero. The raw-score regression equation used for prediction in the social sciences has a slightly different form and uses different symbols:

$$\hat{Y} = a + bX$$

where,

$\hat{Y}$ is the symbol for the predicted value of the dependent variable,
a represents the intercept, or the predicted value of the dependent variable when $X = 0$,
b is the symbol for the slope, or the amount of change in the dependent variable that corresponds to an increase of 1 unit in the independent variable, and
X represents a known value of the independent variable.

You will encounter the terms *regression constant* and *regression coefficient* in the social science literature as well as statistical analysis software such as SPSS. The term *regression constant* is simply another name for the intercept, whereas *regression coefficient* refers to the slope.

Developing the raw-score regression equation requires determining the slope and the intercept. We calculate the intercept using three steps, and we calculate the slope similarly but with an additional fourth step. Here we work through these steps for the MFT in psychology test scores.

For the intercept:

Step 1. Find the *z* score when *X* is zero.

$$z_X = \frac{(X - M_X)}{SD_X} = \frac{0 - 3.175}{0.492} = -6.453$$

Step 2. Use the *z* score to calculate the predicted score on *Y*.

$$z_{\hat{Y}} = (r_{XY})(z_X) = (0.665)(-6.453) = -4.291$$

Step 3. Convert the *z* score to its raw score.

$$\hat{Y} = z_{\hat{Y}}(SD_Y) + M_Y = (-4.291)(12.977) + 160.122 = 104.438$$

This value is the *y* intercept.

Now let's compute the slope. We repeat the first three steps but for an *X* score of 1. This way we can see how the value of *Y* changes as *X* changes from zero to one.

Step 1. $z_X = \dfrac{(X - M_X)}{SD_X} = \dfrac{1 - 3.175}{0.492} = -4.421$

Step 2. $z_{\hat{Y}} = (r_{XY})(z_X) = (0.665)(-4.421) = -2.94$

Step 3. $\hat{Y} = z_{\hat{Y}}(SD_Y) + M_Y = (-2.94)(12.977) + 160.122 = 121.97$

Step 4. Find the slope and use the line to make predictions.

To find the slope, we compare the value of Y when X is zero (104.438) to the value of Y when X was equal to one (121.97). There is an increase of 17.532 points. In other words, as someone's GPA goes up by 1 unit, we can expect a change in MFT score of 17.532 points.

Now we can write the equation for the line:

$$\hat{Y} = 104.438 + 17.532(X)$$

We can use this equation to make predictions. For example, our senior with the GPA of 2.32 would be expected to earn an MFT score of

$$\hat{Y} = 104.438 + 17.532(2.32) = 145.112$$

This value is almost identical to the one we calculated with the z score conversion procedure earlier, and it is only slightly different due to rounding. The value of calculating this equation is that we can now, very easily, use it to predict scores based on any GPA value.

The basis of simple linear regression is the correlation between two variables. Both correlation and regression may be depicted in a scatterplot such as the one below showing the regression of MFT total score on cumulative GPA. (The axes are scaled as they are because MFT total scores range from 120 to 200, and no student had a GPA below 2.0.)

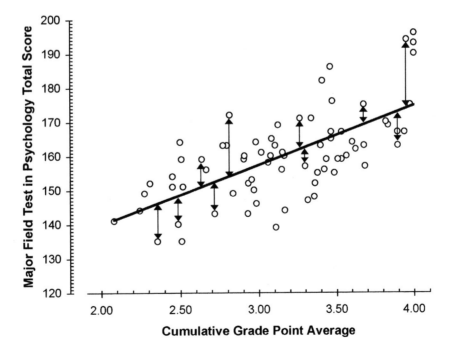

The line in the figure is the *regression line*, also called the *least squares line* and the *line of best fit*. It is the line that corresponds to the regression equation. The regression line is called the least squares line because it minimizes the sum of squared vertical distances between the points and the line (some examples are shown in the scatterplot). It is called the line of best fit because there is no other line that could be drawn to "fit" the data points that could further reduce the sum of the squared vertical distances between the points and the line.

To draw the regression line, you need two points, which you just calculated. It can be helpful to have a third point in order to draw your line. The regression line always passes through the point of means, so use M_X, M_Y (3.175, 160.122) as the third point. If you plug the mean for X into the regression equation, you will get a predicted Y that is slightly different from the mean of Y because of rounding error.

The Standardized Regression Coefficient and Hypothesis Testing with Regression

To compare scores measured on different scales, we standardize the scores onto a common scale (z scores are often used). We can do the same thing with the slope of regression equations that are computed on incompatible data. That is, we can compute the standardized regression coefficient. This coefficient represents the "predicted change in the dependent variable in terms of standard deviations for a 1 standard deviation increase in the independent variable" (text page 374). The coefficient is often called a **beta weight**, and the formula is

$$\beta = (b) \frac{\sqrt{SS_X}}{\sqrt{SS_Y}}$$

As noted in the text, the value of β is the same as the correlation coefficient when we are performing simple linear regression (but only in this situation). So, in this case, β would be 0.665. In addition, the hypothesis test for the standardized regression coefficient is the same as that for the correlation coefficient with simple linear relations.

> Interpretation and Prediction

Regression and Error

As we can see in the scatterplots in this chapter and Chapter 14 of the text, the data points vary around the line of best fit. Except in the case of a perfect correlation, there is always error, or variability, around the regression line. This error can be visually assessed by the quality of the fit of the line to the data.

Look at the scatterplot of the regression of MFT total scores on GPA.

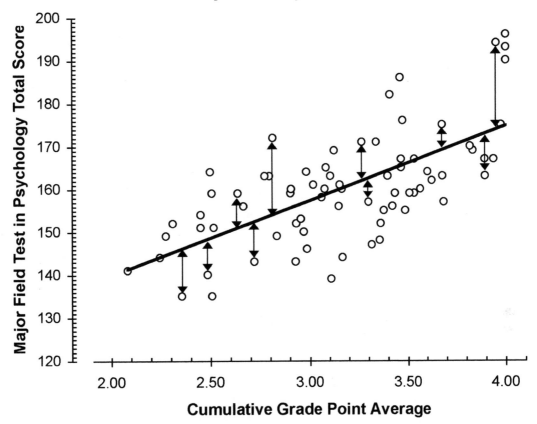

You may think of the vertical distances as errors of prediction, because they represent the differences between the predicted and actual values of the *Y* variable. In fact, the **standard error of the estimate**, a statistic based on these vertical distances, is computed as a measure of the typical error associated with predicting *Y* values using the regression equation.

The standard error of the estimate is a number that captures the average distance of all data points from the regression line, and it is computed when we perform a regression analysis using statistical software.

Applying the Lessons of Correlation to Regression

Regression is a powerful statistical tool, but it shares many of the limitations associated with correlation. You know from your study of Chapter 13 that there may not be a direct causal link between correlated variables. There are any number of other variables that may be responsible for an observed correlation. So, as was true for correlation, regression does not imply causality. As you will be reminded repeatedly in this course and others, a causal relation between an independent variable and a dependent variable may be observed only when participants are randomly assigned to different levels of the independent variable.

Constructing a scatterplot should always be the initial step in the analysis of correlational data. In addition to revealing nonlinearity, a scatterplot will disclose the presence of questionable data points and large variability around the line of best fit.

Regression to the Mean

A final observation about drawing conclusions from regression involves a statistical artifact that is frequently misinterpreted. You may have noticed that the hypothetical student's predicted z score on the MFT (–1.156) is closer to the mean than her GPA expressed as a z score (–1.738). This statistical consequence of multiplying the z score on the independent variable by a correlation coefficient that is less than 1 is called **regression to the mean**. More formally, when the variables in a correlational study are not perfectly correlated, the predicted score on the dependent variable will, on average, always be less extreme than the score on the independent variable; that is, the predicted score will regress toward the mean of the scores on the dependent variable. A failure to appreciate the inevitability of regression to the mean can easily result in flawed interpretations of changes in scores over time.

Proportionate Reduction in Error

The standard error of the estimate is related to the measure of effect size for regression. The effect size for simple linear regression is a measure of the increase in the accuracy of predictions that is achieved by basing those predictions on the correlation between X and Y. In fact, the effect size for regression may be obtained by simply squaring the correlation coefficient (r^2) to produce a statistic called the *coefficient of determination*. However, effect size is perhaps better understood by going through the steps required to compute the **proportionate reduction in error** (*PRE*). Please note that the coefficient of determination and the proportionate reduction in error are two names for the same statistic. However, the calculations involved in determining the PRE, while more time-consuming, are much more informative in terms of illustrating the improvement in prediction accuracy when the regression equation is used.

To compute the proportionate reduction in error, we compare how the mean performs as a predictor to the regression equation as a generator of predictions.

We see on page 381 of the text that the first step in calculating proportionate reduction in error is to compute how much error we experience when we simply use the mean of Y to predict scores. In other words, we compare actual Y scores to the mean of Y as a predictor to see how much error occurs. Clearly, everyone does not score at the mean, so comparing actual scores to the mean as a predictor will generate some error in prediction; we will be wrong much of the time if we use the mean of Y as the prediction for each X score. We are interested in the extent to which the predictions are wrong. Because we will observe errors both above and below the actual Y scores, we square the error values before summing them. This number, the sum of squared error for the mean, is your prediction (and in the text was calculated as 2262).

Next, we take each X score and generate a predicted Y value using the regression equation. These predicted Y scores are then compared to the actual Y scores observed. Again, we have some error in both directions, positive and negative, so we square our errors before summing them. This number is the sum of squared error for the regression equation (and in our text was calculated as 623.425).

The proportionate reduction in error requires that we compare the total squared error for the mean to that for the regression equation. So we take the total squared error for the mean and subtract away the squared error for the regression equation (2262 − 623.425 = 1638.575). This is the reduction in error. Now we want to express the reduction in error as a proportion of total error, so we divide the reduction in error by the total error based on the mean (1638.575/2262). The result is the percent of error we removed by using the regression equation rather than the mean. We hope that this number will be considerable, indicating the added value of computing the regression equation. Of course, the stronger the correlation, the better the regression equation will do in reducing the error of prediction compared to using the mean as the best guess.

> Multiple Regression

As noted above, a simple linear (or bivariate) regression equation is used when the researcher's interest is in predicting the values of a dependent variable from the values of a single independent variable. In **multiple regression**, two or more independent variables are used to predict the values of a dependent variable. In other words, multiple linear regression extends simple linear regression by including at least one additional independent variable in the regression equation. Virtually all dependent variables of interest to researchers in the social sciences are linked in complex ways to multiple independent variables, and for this reason, multiple regression is far more common than bivariate regression in the research literature.

The goal of any regression analysis is to explain as much of the variability in the dependent variable as efficiently as possible. An ideal multiple regression equation includes independent variables that uniquely account for this variability. Such variables are said to be **orthogonal**. In other contexts, "orthogonal" means "at right angles," and this idea is expressed in the context of multiple regression as well when we observe that orthogonal independent variables are related to the dependent variable "from different angles." Conversely, independent variables that overlap in their predictive associations with the dependent variable are said to be *nonorthogonal*.

In multiple regression, the term *slope* is replaced by *partial regression coefficient* and the *intercept* is called the *regression constant*. The form of a raw-score multiple regression equation with three independent variables is as follows:

$$\hat{Y} = a + b_1 X_1 + b_2 X_2 + b_3 X_3$$

where,

$\hat{Y}$ is the predicted value of the dependent (criterion) variable,

a is the regression constant (similar to the y-intercept in simple linear regression),

$b_1 - b_3$ are the unstandardized partial regression coefficients or slopes for the independent variables, and

$X_1 - X_3$ are the values of the independent (predictor) variables.

The multiple regression equation shows each independent variable (X) being multiplied (weighted) by a regression coefficient (b) or slope. The regression coefficient or slope is the amount of change in the predicted value of the dependent variable ($\hat{Y}$) for each increase of one unit in the associated independent variable, *with the effects of all other independent variables held constant.* The *sign* of the coefficient indicates the *direction* of change in the predicted value of the dependent variable: a positive sign denotes an increase, whereas a negative sign indicates a decrease. Values of each independent variable are plugged into the multiple regression equation to predict a value of the dependent variable.

STUDY QUESTIONS

Please label the following statements as either True or False.

1. In simple linear regression, values of the dependent variable are predicted from values of one independent variable.

2. Simple linear regression is not used if a scatterplot of the data reveals a pattern that is curved rather than well-approximated by a straight line.

3. In a scatterplot that includes a regression line, the distance between the data points and the line is indicated by the magnitude of the correlation coefficient: the higher the absolute value of the correlation coefficient, the closer the points to the line.

4. As long as the correlation between two variables is less than perfect, a predicted z score will be closer to the mean than the z score used to predict it.

5. The phrase regression to the mean refers to the fact that scores on the dependent (Y) variable are generally closer to M_Y than scores on the independent (X) variable are to M_X.

6. In simple linear regression, the *intercept* is the value of the dependent (Y) variable when $X = M_X$.

7. In simple linear regression, the *slope* of the regression line is a measure of the amount of change in the dependent variable for each unit of change in the independent variable.

8. If values of one variable may be used to predict values of another variable, then the variables must be causally related.

9. In both simple and *multiple linear regression*, the symbol for the measure of effect size is R^2.

Multiple-Choice Questions

10. Complete the analogy: *Correlation* is to *regression* as:
    a. relation is to causality.
    b. relation is to prediction.
    c. prediction is to relation.
    d. causality is to relation.

11. In **simple linear regression**, scores on _____ independent variable(s) are used to predict scores on _____ dependent variable(s).
    a. one; one
    b. one or more; one
    c. one; one or more
    d. two or more; one

12. In the equation $\hat{Y}$, what does the symbol represent?
    a. actual value of Y when $X = 0$
    b. predicted value of Y when $X = 0$
    c. actual value of Y for a given value of X
    d. predicted value of Y for a given value of X

13. For a small sample of survey respondents, the correlation between number of years of formal education ($M_X = 13.8$, $SD_X = 2.86$) and age when first married ($M_Y = 22.2$, $SD_Y = 5.00$) is 0.844. Chris has never been married and has just completed his 16th and last year of formal education. What age (in years) would you predict for Chris when he marries?
    a. 18.96
    b. 24.06
    c. 25.66
    d. 25.44

14. A scatterplot shows that two variables, X and Y, appear to be linearly related, and the Pearson correlation coefficient computed to quantify this relation is –0.71. From this information, you know that the **slope** of a line drawn to fit the points in the scatterplot is _____.
    a. positive
    b. negative
    c. approximately zero
    d. insufficient information to answer

15. In the equation $\hat{Y}$, what is the symbol for the **intercept**?
    a. $\hat{Y}$
    b. a
    c. b
    d. X

16. In the equation $\hat{Y}$, what is the symbol for the **slope**?
    a. $\hat{Y}$
    b. a
    c. b
    d. X

17. In the equation, $\hat{Y} = a + b(X)$, the symbol a represents the:
    a. predicted value of Y when $X = 0$.
    b. predicted value of X when $Y = 0$.
    c. predicted change in Y when X changes by one unit.
    d. change in X when the predicted value of Y changes by one unit.

18. A certain college requires all psychology majors to take the Major Field Test (MFT) in Psychology published by the Educational Testing Service (ETS) during January of their senior year. Psychology majors may graduate summa cum laude if they have a cumulative GPA of at least 3.75 and a total MFT score at or above the 90th percentile based on national norms published by the ETS. Since implementing this policy, the Psychology Department at this institution has compiled the following statistics:

	MFT Total Score	GPA
M	164.358	3.273
SD	13.892	0.385
r	0.596	

    What is the *slope* of the regression line for predicting MFT total score from GPA?
    a. 0.017
    b. 21.506
    c. 93.970
    d. 164.304

19. The *regression line:*
    a. is used to predict values of the independent variable from values of the dependent variable.
    b. has a positive slope if an increase in the independent variable is associated with a decrease in the dependent variable.
    c. represents a visual equivalent of the equation used to compute the Pearson correlation coefficient.
    d. has a positive slope if an increase in the independent variable is associated with an increase in the dependent variable.

20. A certain college requires all psychology majors to take the Major Field Test (MFT) in Psychology published by the Educational Testing Service (ETS) during January of their senior year. Psychology majors may graduate summa cum laude if they have a cumulative GPA of at least 3.75 and a total MFT score at or above the 90th percentile based on national norms published by the ETS. Since implementing this policy, the Psychology Department at this institution has compiled the following statistics:

	MFT Total Score	GPA
M	164.358	3.273
SD	13.892	0.385
r	0.596	

    What is the predicted MFT total score for a student who has a cumulative GPA of 3.75?
    a. 181.57
    b. 188.311
    c. 174.616
    d. 164.366

21. For two linearly related variables, X and Y, the regression equation is $\hat{Y} = 10 - 0.2(X)$
    For each 10-unit increase in X, what is the predicted change in Y?
    a. increase of 8 units
    b. decrease of 8 units
    c. increase of 2 units
    d. decrease of 2 units

22. A *positive* value for the slope of a regression line indicates that:
    a. as the values of one variable increase, the values of the other variable decrease.
    b. as the values of one variable increase, the values of the other variable also increase.
    c. a large change in the independent variable results in a small change in the dependent variable.
    d. a small change in the independent variable results in a large change in the dependent variable.

23. A *negative* value for the slope of a regression line indicates that:
    a. as the values of one variable increase, the values of the other variable decrease.
    b. as the values of one variable increase, the values of the other variable also increase.
    c. a large change in the independent variable results in a small change in the dependent variable.
    d. a small change in the independent variable results in a large change in the dependent variable.

24. Ignoring sign, a *large* value for the slope of a regression line indicates that:
    a. as the values of one variable increase, the values of the other variable decrease.
    b. as the values of one variable increase, the values of the other variable also increase.
    c. a large change in the independent variable results in a small change in the dependent variable.
    d. a small change in the independent variable results in a large change in the dependent variable.

25. When $X = 0$, the predicted value of Y is _____.
    a. always 0
    b. always 1
    c. the intercept
    d. the slope

26. The statistic that measures the typical distance between the regression line and the data points in a scatterplot is called the _____.
    a. regression constant
    b. regression coefficient
    c. standard error of the estimate
    d. proportionate reduction in error

27. Two or more independent variables are **orthogonal** if they:
    a. make separate and distinct contributions in the prediction of the dependent variable.
    b. are positively correlated with each other as well as with the dependent variable.
    c. are positively correlated with each other but not correlated with the dependent variable.
    d. are negatively correlated with each other but positively correlated with the dependent variable.

28. In multiple regression, the direction of the relation between an independent variable X_1 and the dependent variable Y is given by the sign of:
    a. the square of the multiple correlation coefficient (R^2).
    b. its associated unstandardized regression coefficient (b_1), or slope.
    c. the multiple correlation coefficient (R).
    d. the standard error of the estimate.

29. The symbol for proportionate reduction in error in multiple regression is:
    a. r^2.
    b. R^2.
    c. b.
    d. R.

ANSWERS TO CHAPTER 14 STUDY QUESTIONS

Question Number	Correct Answer	Question Number	Correct Answer
1	T, p. 367	14	b, p. 371
2	T, p. 367	15	b, p. 371
3	T, p. 384	16	c, p. 371
4	T, p. 379	17	a, p. 371
5	F, pp. 369 & 379 [Regression to the mean refers to predicted, not actual, scores on the dependent variable.]	18	b, pp. 371–372
		19	d, pp. 371–373
		20	b, pp. 371–373
6	F, p. 371 [The intercept is the value of Y when $X = 0$.]	21	d, pp. 371–373 [The slope is the amount of change in the Y variable for each 1-unit change in the X variable, so if X changes by 10 units, Y changes by (slope)(10) units. Just multiply the slope, –0.2, by 10.]
7	T, p. 371		
8	F, p. 378		
9	F, pp. 380–384 [In simple linear regression, the symbol used to represent effect size is r^2.]		
10	b, p. 367	22	b, p. 371
11	a, p. 367	23	a, p. 371
12	d, pp. 369–371	24	d, p. 371
13	d, p. 370 [First convert Chris's years of formal education to a z score: $(16 – 13.8) / 2.86 = 0.769$. Then multiply this z score by the correlation coefficient: $(0.844)(0.769)$ to obtain the predicted age when married expressed as a z score (0.649). Finally, convert this z score to an age by multiplying it by SD_Y and adding this product to M_Y: $(0.649)(5) + 22.2 = 25.44$ years.]	25	c, p. 371
		26	c, pp. 377–378
		27	a, p. 386
		28	b, p. 387
		29	b, p. 388

Chi Square and Other Nonparametric Tests

LEARNING OBJECTIVES

After studying this chapter, you should be able to:

1. Define each of the following terms and provide examples that are not in the text: *chi-square test for goodness-of-fit, chi-square test for independence, Cramer's V, contingency table, Spearman rank-order correlation coefficient,* and *Mann-Whitney U test.*
2. Know under what circumstances you would want to use a nonparametric test rather than a parametric test.
3. Distinguish between a chi-square test for goodness-of-fit and a chi-square test for independence and know when you'd want to use each one.
4. Calculate a chi-square test for goodness-of-fit and a chi-square test for independence based on observed and expected frequencies.
5. Determine effect size using Cramer's *V*.
6. Distinguish between a Spearman rank-order correlation coefficient and the Mann-Whitney *U* test, and know when you'd want to use each one.

7. Convert interval data to ordinal data to calculate a Spearman rank-order correlation coefficient and the Mann-Whitney U test.

CHAPTER REVIEW

> Nonparametric Statistics

So far in the text we've worked with parametric statistics. In this chapter, we are introduced to nonparametric statistics. We need to use nonparametric statistics when our research design falls under one of three circumstances:

1. When our dependent variable is nominal
2. When either the independent or dependent variable is ordinal
3. When the sample size is small and we suspect that the underlying population of interest is skewed.

Let's talk about some examples of these previous three situations. For the first situation, imagine that we want to examine the number of people in your class who own pets. We could compare the number of people who own pets compared to those who don't. Unlike a t-test, our dependent variable is not an interval variable—either students own a pet or they don't—which means that we need to use a parametric test.

For the second example, we'd need to use an ordinal variable or a ranked variable. For example, imagine we are looking at scores on a midterm based on how much time people spent studying. We could rank the amount of time people in the class spent studying (most time—1st place, 2nd place, 3rd place, etc.) and compare scores on the exam.

Our last example would occur if the sample size is small and the underlying population is skewed. In other words, the sample is somewhat unusual in nature. For example, imagine we wanted to look at the reaction times of male runners who won a gold medal in the Olympics. In this case, there are not a lot of male gold medal runners, so we would end up with a small sample size. Further, the underlying population would probably not be normal.

Although nonparametric tests are useful because they allow us to perform statistical tests when we ordinarily could not, they have a number of limitations. For one thing, we cannot calculate confidence intervals and effect-size measures. In addition, we are more likely to make a Type II error because such tests have less statistical power than parametric tests. Lastly, it is almost always best to use interval data to explain our findings rather than nominal or ordinal data.

> ## Chi-Square Tests

Chi-Square Test for Goodness-of-Fit

In this chapter, we will discuss two different types of chi-square nonparametric hypothesis tests. The first is the **chi-square test for goodness-of-fit,** which we use when we have one nominal variable. This test examines whether the pattern of observed data deviates from what we would expect by chance. If our data is different enough than what we would expect by chance, we can reject the null hypothesis. For this test, we'll be using the chi-square statistic, χ^2, which is based on the chi-square distribution. This is similar to when we used the F statistic and the F distribution for our ANOVAs and the t statistic and t distribution for a t-test.

For this test, we only have one variable that's categorical with two or more categories into which participants are placed. The chi-square goodness-of-fit test gives us a measure of how good the fit is between the observed data in the various categories of a single nominal variable and what we would expect based on the null hypothesis.

Before we discuss how to calculate a chi-square test for goodness of fit, let's discuss an example. Imagine that we want to know whether students in our class are more likely (or less) to have pets than would be expected by chance. Let's say that we have 100 total students in the class, and 65 have pets whereas 35 do not. So, let's go through the six-step process.

Pet Category	Number of Classmates
Students with at least 1 pet	65
Students with no pets	35

Step 1. Identify the populations, distribution, and assumption.

There are two populations when conducting a chi-square: the frequency of participants in the cells based on what we have observed for our study and the frequency of participants in cells based on what we would expect by chance, the null hypothesis. Because we're looking at frequencies and we have just one variable, we know that our distribution is a chi-square distribution and the particular test is the goodness-of-fit.

For this test we have four different assumptions. We first assume that we are working with a nominal variable. For our example, we are looking at the number of pet owners compared to those without pets, so we know that we fall under this assumption. The second assumption is that each observation must be independent of all other observations. In other words, we can't have the same observation in more than one category. For example, no student in the class can be both a pet owner and not a pet owner—you can be one or the other. So, this assumption will be no problem. The third assumption is that all participants should be randomly selected. Although our sample is not randomly selected because all participants are coming from the same classroom, if we meet all of the other assumptions, we could still go forward with the test. This will just limit our ability to generalize beyond our sample. Lastly, we need a minimum of at least 5 (preferably 10) participants in each cell. For our sample, we have 65 with pets and 35 without—both numbers are greater than 10, so we can go ahead with the chi-square test.

Step 2. State the null and research hypotheses.

For chi-square tests, we state the hypothesis in words rather than symbols. So, in this case:

> Null hypothesis: The number of students with pets compared to those without pets is what we would expect by chance.

> Research hypothesis: The number of students with pets compared to those without pets is different than what we would expect by chance.

Step 3. Determine the characteristics of the comparison distribution.

Our next step is to determine our degrees of freedom. For chi-square hypothesis tests, degrees of freedom are based on the number of categories, or cells, in which participants can be counted rather than the number of participants overall. In our case, we have two categories—those who own pets and those who do not. The formula to *calculate the degrees of freedom in a chi-square is the number of categories minus 1: $df_{\chi^2} = k - 1$.* In this case, k is the number of categories, and in our case, $df_{\chi^2} = 2 - 1 = 1$.

Step 4. Determine critical values or cutoffs.

We use the chi-square table to determine the cutoff or critical value. Because a chi-square can never be negative, there is only one critical value, even when we have a two-tailed test. The full table can be found in Appendix B of the text. All we need is to find our degrees of freedom in the first column (which is 1 for our example) and then look for the p value, which is usually 0.05. For our example then, our critical value is 3.84.

Step 5. Calculate the test statistic.

To calculate the test statistic, we need to know our formula which is: $\chi^2 = \Sigma [(O - E)^2/E]$. The O in the formula refers to the observed frequencies (or the data we've collected), and the E refers to the expected frequencies. In some examples, you will be told what the expected frequencies would be. In our example, let's assume that students in the class are equally likely to have a pet as they are to not have a pet. In other words, let's say that either having or not having a pet is equally likely. Alternatively, you could have been given the proportion of the general population with pets and go with that instead. However, assuming it's equally likely, we could create the following table:

Pet Category	Observed (O)	Expected (E)
Students with at least 1 pet	65	50
Students with no pets	35	50

Now that we have our observed and expected frequencies, we can work with our formula. We will need to subtract the expected frequencies from the observed frequencies and square the difference. Finally, we'll divide that value by the expected frequency (in our case, divide the obtained value by 50). We can work out these steps in another table such as the following:

Pet Category	Observed (O)	Expected (E)	$O - E$	$(O - E)^2$	$(O - E)^2/E$
Students with at least 1 pet	65	50	15	225	4.5
Students with no pets	35	50	−15	225	4.5

Our final step is to sum the numbers in the right-most column, which is: $4.5 + 4.5 = 9.0$. This is our test statistic, which we will use to compare with our cutoff.

Step 6. Make a decision.

Because our test statistic, 9.0, is greater than our critical value, 3.84, we can reject the null hypothesis. In this case, we can say that students in the class have significantly more pets than would be expected by chance. To report the results, we provide the degrees of freedom, the value of the test statistic, and whether the p value was greater or less than the value of the cutoff. We also provide the sample size with our degrees of freedom. For our example, we would provide the following, $\chi^2 = (1, N = 100) = 9.0$, $p < 0.05$.

> Chi-Square Test for Independence

The chi-square test for independence is used when we have more than one nominal variable. The test allows us to determine whether the two variables are independent of one another. Imagine we want to know if getting into the elite state junior orchestra depends on whether students received special music lessons from a tutor. To find out, we design a study so that some students who are planning on trying out for the orchestra get lessons while others do not. We then look to see who was accepted into the orchestra. Based on our results, imagine that we construct the following table:

	Accepted into Orchestra	Not Accepted into Orchestra	Totals
Received music lessons	22	53	75
No lessons	8	67	75
Totals	30	120	

This table is called a *contingency table*.

We would use a chi-square test for independence because we have two nominal variables (orchestra status and music lessons). Our frequencies refer to observed frequencies. The test will allow us to determine if getting accepted into the orchestra depends on whether the students received special lessons. Just like our previous tests, we have six steps of hypothesis testing, which we will review:

Step 1. Identify the populations, distribution, and assumptions.

Population 1 refers to students who received music lessons, and population 2 refers to students who did not receive music lessons. Because these are nominal variables, we know that we will need to use the chi-square distribution. Further, there is more than one nominal variable, so we know that we will need to use the chi-square test of independence.

As with the chi-square test for goodness-of-fit, we have four assumptions. First, we know that we are working with two nominal variables. We also pass our second assumption because each participant is only in one cell—there is no overlap. Third, all participants should be randomly selected. In our case, participants were not randomly selected from all students trying out for the orchestra. We concentrated on one school district. As a result, we will need to be cautious about our conclusions. Finally, because we have more than five times as many participants as cells (150 total), we have a large enough sample size.

Step 2. State the null and research hypotheses.

As with our chi-square for goodness-of-fit, we state our hypotheses in words rather than with words and symbols. Because the chi-square test for independence tests for whether one variable depends on the other, we will use such words in our hypotheses. So, for our example:

Null Hypothesis: Getting accepted into the state orchestra is independent of whether students received special music lessons.

Research Hypothesis: Getting accepted into the state orchestra depends on whether students received special music lessons.

Step 3. Determine the characteristics of the comparison distribution.

The formula to determine the degrees of freedom for the chi-square test for independence is: $df_{\chi^2} = (k_{row} - 1)(k_{column} - 1)$. For our example, the row variable is whether students received music lessons, and there are two levels. So, we calculate for the row variable as: $(k_{row} - 1) = 2 - 1 = 1$. Our column variable is whether students were accepted into the orchestra, and there are also two levels, $(k_{column} - 1) = 2 - 1 = 1$. When we put both together, we know that $df_{\chi^2} = 1$.

Step 4. Determine the critical values, or cutoffs.

Now that we know our degrees of freedom, we can determine our critical value. For our example, we'll keep the p level at 0.05 and look at the table in Appendix B of the text under 1 degree of freedom. When we do that, we'll find that our critical value is 3.84. As a result, to reject the null hypothesis, our test statistic must be greater than 3.84, as pictured in the following figure from the text:

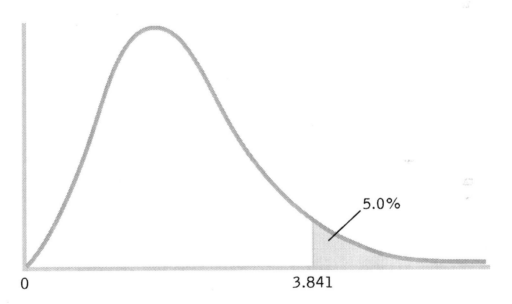

Step 5. Calculate the test statistic.

For this step, we will need to determine what the expected frequencies will be. For our example, we can look at the total number of students who made it into the orchestra (30) and divide that number by the total number of students who tried out for the orchestra (150). This means that the acceptance rate is 20.0% (30/150) for our sample. If receiving music lessons does not affect the outcome, then we would expect the same percentage regardless of the music-lesson condition. We also know that 80% of people did not gain acceptance into the orchestra. Therefore, we expect that 80% of people regardless of the music condition would not get into the orchestra. Because we would expect 20% of the 75 people who received lessons to get accepted, our expected frequency becomes: $(0.20)(75) = 15$. This is also the same frequency for those who did not receive lessons. Now, we expect 80% of the students in each music condition group to not get into the orchestra, so this expected frequency becomes: $(0.80)(75) = 60$. Now, we can go ahead and create a table of expected frequencies based on this information.

	EXPECTED		
	Accepted into orchestra	Not accepted into orchestra	Totals
Received music lessons	15	60	75
No lessons	15	60	75
Totals	30	120	

We could have calculated the expected frequency for each cell using a formula instead. To do this, we divide the cell's column total by the grand total and multiply that by the row total. In other words, the formula is: $(Total_{column}/N)(Total_{row})$. In our example, the grand total (N) is 150. Our row total is 75. Our column total will be either 30 or 120 depending on which cell we are looking at. For those who have been accepted into the orchestra, our calculation becomes: $(30/150)(75) = 15$. For those who have not been accepted into the orchestra, our calculation becomes: $(120/150)(75) = 60$.

Our next step is to use the formula that we used for the chi-square goodness-of-fit test. If you recall, our formula was: $\chi^2 = \Sigma\,[(O - E)^2/E]$. So, we can create a new table that includes all of the information with observed and expected frequencies together, so we can complete the formula.

Category	Observed (O)	Expected (E)	$O - E$	$(O - E)^2$	$(O - E)^2/E$
Lessons, accepted	22	15	7.0	49	3.27
Lessons, not accepted	53	60	−7.0	49	0.82
No lessons, accepted	8	15	−7.0	49	3.27
No lessons, not accepted	67	60	7.0	49	0.82

Then, we can add up everything in our right-most column: $(3.27 + 0.82 + 3.27 + 0.82) = 8.18$.

Step 6. Make a decision.

Because 8.18 is greater than 3.84, we can reject the null hypothesis. This means that getting into the orchestra depends on the whether the students received music lessons. When reporting the findings, we would use the same format as the chi-square goodness-of-fit and include the degrees of freedom, the total number of participants, the test statistic, and whether the test statistic is greater or less than the critical value, $\chi^2 = (1, N = 150) = 8.18, p < 0.05$.

Cramer's V, the Effect Size for Chi Square

Even if we are able to reject the null hypothesis, the results of the hypothesis test alone do not tell us how large the effect is. Before we can say that our findings are important, we need to calculate **Cramer's V** or **Cramer's phi, ϕ**, which is the standard effect size used with the chi-square for independence. The formula for *Cramer's V* is:

$$\sqrt{\frac{X^2}{(N)(df_{row/column})}}$$

For this formula, χ^2 is the test statistic that was calculated, N is the total number of participants in the study, and $df_{row/column}$ is the smaller of either the degrees of freedom for the row or column variable.

Let's calculate Cramer's V for our example. In our previous example, $\chi^2 = 8.18$, there were 150 participants, and the degrees of freedom for both variables was 1. If we plug these numbers into the formula:

$$\sqrt{\frac{X^2}{(N)(df_{row/column})}} = \sqrt{\frac{8.18}{(150)(1)}} = \sqrt{0.0545} = 0.23$$

We can use the Table 15-9 from the text to determine how large the effect is.

TABLE 15-9. Conventions for Determining Effect Size Based on Cramer's V

Jacob Cohen (1992) developed guidelines to determine whether particular effect sizes should be considered small, medium, or large. The effect-size guidelines vary depending on the size of the contingency table. There are different guidelines based on whether the smaller of the two degrees of freedom (row or column) is 1, 2, or 3.

Effect Size	When $df_{row/column} = 1$	When $df_{row/column} = 2$	When $df_{row/column} = 3$
Small	0.10	0.07	0.06
Medium	0.30	0.21	0.17
Large	0.50	0.35	0.29

Based on this information, because Cramer's V is larger than guidelines for a small effect but smaller than a medium effect, we would probably say that we have a small-to-medium effect. Cramer's V would then get added at the end when we report our results: $\chi^2 = (1, N = 150) = 8.18, p < 0.05$, Cramer's $V = 0.23$.

> Other Nonparametric Tests

We cannot use parametric tests when data are ordinal. Ordinal data are rank-ordered. For example, we might want to look at variables from individuals who were in the top 10 in a race. Based on such data, we can't have a normal distribution that is bell-shaped because there will only be one individual at every value (e.g., one person in first place, one person in second place, etc.). Here, we'll be learning about two different alternatives to the parametric tests when we have ordinal data. These nonparametric tests aren't any more difficult than the parametric tests. We just need to know when to use them and recognize when we are working with ordinal data.

Spearman Rank-Order Correlation Coefficient

The **Spearman rank-order correlation coefficient,** which is a nonparametric statistic that quantifies the association between two ordinal variables. The Spearman rank-order correlation coefficient is also known as Spearman's rho and is symbolized by the coefficient, r_s.

As an example, imagine we want to know whether the class ranking of students is related to their SAT verbal scores. For the purposes of our example, let's stick to a sample of 12 students. We receive the class rankings, which are ordinal by nature. However, the SAT verbal scores are not ordinal. Because a Spearman correlation can only be used if both variables are ordinal, we will need to transform the SAT verbal scores to ranking as well.

To transform the scores to rankings, we should organize the SAT verbal scores from highest to lowest and rank them. If there are students that share the same SAT verbal score, we take the average of the two ranks that the participants would hold, as the following table shows.

Student	SAT Verbal Score	SAT Rank
Emily	710	1
Jacob	680	2
Danielle	660	3
Tyra	630	4
Simeon	570	5
Natasha	560	6.5
Max	560	6.5
Christopher	510	8
Tabitha	500	9
Gordon	490	10
Gwendolyn	470	11
Sam	450	12

In this table, we can see that both Natasha and Max earned a 560 on the SAT verbal. So, we'd take the average of the two ranks that they would hold if the scores were different $(6 + 7)/2 = 6.5$. As you can see, both students would receive a rank of 6.5. Now that we have converted our score to ranks, we can combine this information with the class-ranking data.

Student	SAT Rank	Class Rank
Emily	1	1
Jacob	2	5
Danielle	3	3
Tyra	4	7
Simeon	5	2
Natasha	6.5	9
Max	6.5	11
Christopher	8	4
Tabitha	9	12
Gordon	10	6
Gwendolyn	11	8
Sam	12	10

Now that our data are ready we can work toward calculating the correlation. Just like we did with a Pearson correlation, we test the null hypothesis that the correlation coefficient is 0. If we reject the null hypothesis, it means that the correlation is significantly different from 0. We can also think of the Spearman correlation coefficient as a descriptive statistic.

To calculate the correlation, we will need the formula which is:

$$r_s = 1 - \frac{6\left(\Sigma D^2\right)}{N\left(N^2 - 1\right)}$$

For this formula, D refers to the difference in rank and N refers to the sample size, which is 12 for our example. This means that we need to calculate D and square it for each participant.

Student	SAT Rank	Class Rank	Difference (D)	Squared Difference (D^2)
Emily	1	1	0	0
Jacob	2	5	–3	9
Danielle	3	3	0	0
Tyra	4	7	–3	9
Simeon	5	2	3	9
Natasha	6.5	9	–2.5	6.25
Max	6.5	11	–4.5	20.25
Christopher	8	4	4	16
Tabitha	9	12	–3	9
Gordon	10	6	4	16
Gwendolyn	11	8	3	9
Sam	12	10	2	4

Now that we've calculated D and D^2 we can go back to our formula and take the sum of these differences: $D^2 = (0 + 9 + 0 + 9 + 9 + 6.25 + 20.25 + 16 + 9 + 16 + 9 + 4) = 107.5$. Then, we plug this into our formula:

$$r_s = 1 - \frac{6\left(\Sigma D^2\right)}{N\left(N^2 - 1\right)}$$

$$= 1 - \frac{6(107.5)}{12\left(12^2 - 1\right)} = 1 - \frac{645}{12(144 - 1)} = 1 - \frac{645}{1716} = 1 - 0.376 = 0.62$$

Based on our example, the Spearman correlation coefficient is 0.62. The Spearman correlation is similar to the Pearson correlation in that it can range from –1 to 1. The sign indicates the direction of the correlation rather than the strength of the correlation. Because we have obtained a positive correlation, we know that as one ranking increases so does the other ranking. In our example, as class rankings increase, so do SAT rankings.

Also remember that whenever we are working with any correlation—whether it is a Pearson correlation or a Spearman correlation coefficient—that we cannot infer causation. Even though in our example we have a fairly strong correlation, indicating that class rankings positively correlate with SAT rankings, we cannot say that one variable caused the other one to occur. As you probably recall, we can never know with a correlation whether variable A caused variable B, variable B caused variable A, or whether some other variable causes the others. In our example, probably some other variable such as IQ or overall time spent studying caused the rankings in class and SAT scores.

Mann-Whitney U Test

When we have two groups that are not related, we would usually use the independent-samples t test. However, if we do not meet the assumptions of an independent-samples t test, we need to use a nonparametric test. In this case, we would use the **Mann-Whitney U test**, which is a nonparametric hypothesis test used when there are two groups, a between-groups design, and an ordinal dependent variable. Our parametric independent-samples t test was symbolized with t; for a Mann-Whitney U test, it is symbolized with U.

For our example, imagine that we want to compare the SAT verbal scores of males and females in our class. Although our data are interval, our sample is too small and not normally distributed so we should use a nonparametric test. We will need to convert our data into ranks. Let's first divide our data into the two groups for male and female students.

Female Students	SAT Score
Emily	710
Danielle	660
Tyra	630
Natasha	560
Tabitha	500
Gwendolyn	470

Male Students	SAT Score
Jacob	680
Simeon	570
Max	560
Christopher	510
Gordon	490
Sam	450

We'll now continue with our six steps of hypothesis testing just like we did for our parametric tests.

Step 1. Determine the assumptions.

For a Mann-Whitney U test, there are three assumptions. First, our data must be ordinal. At the moment, our data is interval, which we will need to convert to ordinal once we are prepared to calculate the test statistic. Second, we should have random selection. Because our data are not randomly selected, we will want to be very cautious about generalizing from our results. Third, no ranks should be tied. Although not ideal, there is only one tie in our data. As a result, it is probably safe to proceed with our example.

Step 2. State the null and research hypotheses.

For a Mann-Whitney U test, we state the null and research hypotheses in words rather than symbols. So for our example:

> Null Hypothesis: Male and female students do not differ in SAT verbal scores.

> Research Hypothesis: Male and female students differ in SAT verbal scores.

Step 3. Determine the characteristics of the comparison distribution.

The Mann-Whitney U test compares the two distributions of our two samples. In our case, we compare the SAT verbal scores of the six female students to the six male students. There is no comparison distribution in the sense of a parametric test.

Step 4. Determine critical values or cutoffs.

We can determine the critical values by looking at Tables B.8A and B in the appendix of the textbook. There are two versions of the table—one for a one-tailed test and one for a two-tailed test. Based on our research hypothesis and since we don't have a more specific hypothesis regarding the verbal SAT scores, we'll go with a two-tailed test. We also only have critical values for a p level of 0.05. Next, to determine the critical value, we'll need the sample size of each group. In this table, we find the sample size for the first group across the top row and the sample size for the second group in the left-hand column. With this information, our cutoff is 5. For a nonparametric test, we want our test statistic to be equal to or smaller than our critical value. For our example, this means that we want our test statistic to be equal to or smaller than 5.

Step 5. Calculate the test statistic.

To calculate our test statistic, we first need to organize our data. We need to list our data from highest to lowest in a single column and then rank the data. Note that we had one set of tied scores (those of Natasha and Max), and we needed to average the ranks of the two scores.

Student	SAT Score	SAT Rank
Emily	710	1
Jacob	680	2
Danielle	660	3
Tyra	630	4
Simeon	570	5
Natasha	560	6.5
Max	560	6.5
Christopher	510	8
Tabitha	500	9
Gordon	490	10
Gwendolyn	470	11
Sam	450	12

Next, we'll want to list which group (Male or Female) each rank belongs to and then separate the ranks by group.

Student	SAT Score	SAT Rank	Gender (*F* vs. *M*)	*F* Ranks	*M* Ranks
Emily	710	1	*F*	1	
Jacob	680	2	*M*		2
Danielle	660	3	*F*	3	
Tyra	630	4	*F*	4	
Simeon	570	5	*M*		5
Natasha	560	6.5	*F*	6.5	
Max	560	6.5	*M*		6.5
Christopher	510	8	*M*		8
Tabitha	500	9	*F*	9	
Gordon	490	10	*M*		10
Gwendolyn	470	11	*F*	11	
Sam	450	12	*M*		12

Our next step is to sum up the ranks for each group, including subscripts (F and M) to indicate which group is which.

$$\Sigma R_F = 1 + 3 + 4 + 6.5 + 9 + 11 = 34.5$$

$$\Sigma R_M = 2 + 5 + 6.5 + 8 + 10 + 12 = 43.5$$

Now, we'll need our formula for our test statistic. We calculate separate test statistics for each group. For our first group (F), the test statistic is calculated by:

$$U_F = \left(n_F\right)\left(n_M\right) + \frac{\left(n_F\right)\left(n_F + 1\right)}{2} - \Sigma R_F$$

$$= (6)(6) + \frac{6(6+1)}{2} - 34.5 = 36 + \frac{6(7)}{2} - 34.5 = 36 + 21 - 34.5 = 22.5$$

The test statistic for our second group (M) is calculated by:

$$U_M = \left(n_M\right)\left(n_F\right) + \frac{\left(n_M\right)\left(n_M + 1\right)}{2} - \Sigma R_M$$

$$= (6)(6) = \frac{6(6+1)}{2} - 43.5 = 36 + \frac{6(7)}{2} - 43.5 = 36 + 21 - 43.5 = 13.5$$

Our test statistic for our first group, U_F, is 22.5, and our test statistic for our second group, U_M, is 13.5.

Step 6. Make a decision.

We then compare only our smaller test statistic, 13.5, to the critical value of 5. Because our test statistic is not smaller than our critical value, we fail to reject the null hypothesis. We cannot conclude that the SAT verbal scores of the female students are different from those of the male students. When writing this up, we report only the smaller test statistic and we do not include the subscript. The statistic will read, $U = 13.5$, $p > 0.05$.

STUDY QUESTIONS

1. A nonparametric test should be used when the dependent variable is measured on a(n) _____ scale.
   a. nominal or an ordinal
   b. nominal or an interval
   c. ordinal or an interval
   d. nominal, ordinal, or interval

2. For cases in which the assumptions of a parametric test are clearly violated:
   a. the equivalent nonparametric test is often more powerful.
   b. the equivalent, but less powerful, nonparametric test should be conducted.
   c. the parametric test should be conducted to avoid sacrificing statistical power.
   d. there is no alternative but to replace the independent and dependent variables.

3. To maximize statistical power and minimize the probability of committing a Type II error, researchers should measure the dependent variable on a(n) _____ scale whenever possible.
   a. nominal
   b. ordinal
   c. interval
   d. nonparametric

4. Which of the following is a (are) consequence(s) of analyzing your data with a nonparametric test?
   a. Confidence intervals may not be calculated.
   b. There is an increase in the probability of making a Type II error.
   c. Effect size measures may not be available.
   d. All of these are consequences.

5. Which of the following is the best advice to give a researcher whose sample size is small and who suspects that the population distribution of dependent variable values is extremely skewed?
   a. Use a parametric test.
   b. Use a nonparametric test.
   c. Use either a parametric test or a nonparametric test.
   d. Re-design the study, because there are no appropriate statistical tests for this research situation.

6. The **chi-square test for goodness-of-fit** is used to test hypotheses about _____ variable(s).
   a. one ordinal
   b. one nominal
   c. two ordinal
   d. two nominal

7. The **chi-square test for independence** is used to test hypotheses about _____ variable(s).
   a. one ordinal
   b. one nominal
   c. two ordinal
   d. two nominal

8. The chi-square statistic is based on a comparison between the:
   a. mean scores of two independent samples of observations.
   b. median ranks of two independent samples of observations.
   c. frequency of an observation and the frequency expected by chance.
   d. number of interval variables in two or more nonoverlapping categories.

9. Which of the following is/are an assumption(s) for the chi-square tests?
   a. Groups must have equal variances.
   b. Observations must be independent.
   c. Variables must be measured on an interval scale.
   d. Observations must be sampled from a normal population.

10. According to Delucchi (1983), which of the following is the most important principle regarding low expected cell frequencies in the chi-square tests?
    a. There should be at least five times as many individuals (participants) as there are cells.
    b. The tests should not be used if any of the expected cell frequencies is less than 10.
    c. The tests should not be used if any of the expected cell frequencies is less than 5.
    d. The tests have adequate power even with expected frequencies as low as 1.

11. Which of the following is the formula for finding the degrees of freedom associated with a chi-square test for goodness-of-fit?
    a. (number of columns – 1) (number of rows – 1)
    b. (number of columns – 1) / (number of rows – 1)
    c. number of categories – 1
    d. number of participants – 1

12. How is a chi-square table used in hypothesis testing?
    a. A computed chi-square statistic is compared to a critical value of chi-square from the table.
    b. The table provides estimates of power for different significance levels and effect sizes.
    c. The table provides estimates of effect size for different levels of power and significance.
    d. A p value for a computed chi-square statistic is compared to the appropriate p level for the specified degrees of freedom.

13. Portion of a Chi-Square Table

df	Significance Level		
	0.10	0.05	0.01
1	2.706	3.841	6.635
2	4.605	5.992	9.211
3	6.252	7.815	11.345
4	7.780	9.488	13.277
5	9.237	11.071	15.087

Suppose that a researcher computed the chi-square statistic in a test of the null hypothesis that four brands of a product are equally preferred in a population of potential consumers. If the test is conducted at the 0.01 level of significance and the computed value of chi-square is 10.07, then the null hypothesis should:
    a. be rejected because 10.07 is greater than 6.252.
    b. be rejected because 10.07 is greater than 7.780.
    c. not be rejected because 10.07 is less than 11.345.
    d. not be rejected because 10.07 is less than 13.277.

14. Suppose that the results of a large national survey showed the following prevalence of psychological disorders in the adult population of the United States:

Anxiety disorders	15%
Drug and alcohol dependence	20%
Affective disorders	10%
Psychosis	2%
No diagnosed disorder	53%

To test whether these disorders are distributed among college students as they are among adults, a clinical psychologist gathers information from a representative sample of 1000 students from U.S. colleges. In this example, the expected frequency distribution is:
   a. the number of students in each of the diagnostic categories.
   b. the number of students in each of the diagnostic categories, expressed as percentages.
   c. the distribution of percentages reported for adults, converted to frequencies per 1000.
   d. impossible to determine from the information provided.

15. Steinman (2006) compared the rate of twinning in mothers who do not consume animal products (a vegan diet) to that of mothers in the general population. Suppose that 2% of mothers in the general population give birth to twins. Suppose further that Steinman studied the birth records of 1000 vegan mothers and observed just five (5) births of twins. What is the expected frequency of twins in the sample of vegan mothers?
   a. $(0.02)(1000) = 20$
   b. $(0.05)(1000) = 50$
   c. $1000 / 5 = 200$
   d. $(0.02)(0.05)(1000) = 1$

16. Which of the following is the formula for computing the chi-square statistic?

   a. $\chi^2 = \dfrac{Total_{column}}{N}(Total_{row})$ b. $\chi^2 = \Sigma\left[\dfrac{(O-E)^2}{E}\right]$

   c. $\chi^2 = \Sigma\left[\dfrac{(O-E)^2}{O}\right]$ d. $\chi^2 = \Sigma\sqrt{\dfrac{(O-E)^2}{O}}$

17. In a market survey of 99 respondents, a researcher tested the null hypothesis that three brands are equally preferred in the population. The researcher found that 40 respondents preferred Brand A, 35 stated a preference for Brand B, and 24 preferred Brand C. Which of the following represents an appropriate step in the calculation of the chi-square statistic?
    a. $(40 - 35)^2 / 35$
    b. $(40 - 35)^2 / 24$
    c. $(40 - 33)^2 / 33$
    d. $(40 - 33)^2 / 40$

18. A significant chi-square hypothesis test means that:
    a. at least some of the cells' observed frequencies are significantly different from their corresponding expected frequencies.
    b. the variability among the scores for one nominal variable is significantly different from the variability among the scores for at least one other nominal variable.
    c. the number of participants is at least five times greater than the number of cells in the contingency table.
    d. the expected frequencies in any given column of cells are significantly different from the expected frequencies in any given row of cells.

19. A student at a Canadian university conducted a survey of the food preferences (vegetarian, vegan, or neither) and country of origin (Canada, the United States, or other) of 100 students at her university. To test whether food preference and country of origin are related in the population, she should conduct a(n) _____.
    a. chi-square test for independence
    b. independent-samples t test
    c. one-way between-groups analysis of variance
    d. chi-square test for goodness of fit

20. The table of cells for a chi-square test for independence is called a:
    a. χ^2 summary table.
    b. cross-tabulation.
    c. chi-square distribution.
    d. contingency table.

21. For any cell in a contingency table, the expected frequency is the number of observations you would expect in that cell if the:
    a. variables are independent.
    b. variables are not independent.
    c. population means are the same.
    d. population means are not the same.

22. *Unlike* a chi-square for goodness-of-fit, a chi-square test for independence requires that you compute differences between observed and expected frequencies for each combination of categories, that is, for each _____ of the contingency table.
    a. cell
    b. row
    c. column
    d. variable

23. Which of the following is the formula for determining degrees of freedom for the chi-square test for independence?
    a. $N - 1$
    b. number of cells $- 1$
    c. $(k_{column} - 1)(k_{row} - 1)$
    d. $(N)(df_{row/column})$

24. A researcher hypothesized that the most intense facial displays of emotion are negative emotions expressed on the left side of the face. Accordingly, the researcher made full-face photographs of an actor either displaying a happy or an angry expression, then used imaging software to create composite photographs of the left and right sides of each face. A total of 68 participants selected one of the four composite photographs identified in the following table as the most intense facial display of emotion. The expected frequencies are in parentheses.

    | | Expression | | |
Photograph	Happy	Angry	Total
Left Side	8	26	34
Right Side	20	14	34
Total	28	40	68

    What is the expected frequency in the cell that corresponds to the *Happy* expression displayed on the *Left Side* of the face?
    a. 8
    b. (8 / 28)(68) = 19.43
    c. (28 / 68)(34) = 14
    d. (8 / 20)(28) = 11.2

25. The following formula is used to compute the _____ in a contingency table.

    $$\frac{Total_{column}}{N}(Total_{row})$$

    a. degrees of freedom
    b. expected frequency of a cell
    c. observed frequency of a cell
    d. chi-square statistic

26. The _____ may be computed by dividing the column total ($Total_{column}$) by the total number of participants (N) and multiplying this quotient by the row total ($Total_{row}$).
    a. observed frequency for a given cell
    b. effect size for a chi-square test
    c. chi-square test statistic
    d. expected frequency for a given cell

27. Which of the following is the standard effect size used for a chi-square test for independence?
    a. the adjusted standardized residual
    b. the phi coefficient
    c. R^2
    d. Cramer's V

28. Which of the following is the formula used to compute the measure of effect size for a chi-square test for independence?

    a. $\sqrt{\dfrac{\chi^2}{df}}$

    b. $\sqrt{\dfrac{\chi^2}{N}}$

    c. $\sqrt{\dfrac{\chi^2}{(N)(df_{row/column})}}$

    d. $\dfrac{\sqrt{\chi^2}}{(N)(df_{row/column})}$

29. Imagine you run an ice-cream store, and you want to determine whether the rankings of your ten flavors are related to the rankings of your ten ice-cream toppings (e.g., whipped cream, hot fudge, etc.). Based on this data, it would be best to choose a _____ test. More specifically, we should use a _____.
    a. parametric test; Pearson correlation coefficient
    b. nonparametric test; Wilcoxon signed-rank test
    c. nonparametric test; Spearman rank-order correlation coefficient
    d. parametric test; paired-samples t test

30. The **Spearman rank-order correlation coefficient** is a nonparametric statistic that quantifies the association between:
    a. two interval variables.
    b. two nominal variables.
    c. two ordinal variables.
    d. two independent variables.

31. What would the following data look like if we converted these IQ scores to rankings (from lowest to highest)? The raw data are: 72, 98, 98, 105, 115, 137.
    a. 1, 2, 3, 4, 5, 6
    b. 1, 2.5, 2.5, 4, 5, 6
    c. 1, 2, 3, 4.5, 4.6, 6
    d. 1, 2, 2, 4, 5, 6

32. The formula for Spearman's correlation coefficient, r_s, is:

    a. $1 - \dfrac{\sum D}{N(N^2 - 1)}$

    b. $\dfrac{6(\sum D^2)}{N(N^2 - 1)}$

    c. $1 - \dfrac{N(\sum D^2)}{N - 1}$

    d. $1 - \dfrac{6(\sum D^2)}{N(N^2 - 1)}$

33. Imagine you want to calculate the Spearman's correlation coefficient of rankings of height and weight for a group of five individuals. Although you have their rankings for heights, you will need to convert the weight data into ordinal data. Be sure to rank the weights from highest to lowest. What is the correlation?

Participant	Height	Weight
A	1	205
B	2	189
C	3	210
D	4	142
E	5	110

    a. 0.30
    b. 0.52
    c. 0.15
    d. 0.70

34. Which of the following statements is NOT true about the Spearman correlation coefficient?

    a. It ranges from –1 to 1.
    b. If the sign is negative, it means that the relationship between the two variables is weak.
    c. A correlation of 0 indicates that there is no relationship between the two variables.
    d. If the ranks of one variable are the same as the ranks of the second variable, Spearman's correlation coefficient would equal 1.

35. As an avid fan of NASCAR racing, you want to determine whether American cars ranked higher in the race than non-American cars. Based on this information, it would be best to choose a _____ test. More specifically, we should use a(n)_____.

    a. parametric test; independent-samples t test
    b. parametric test; Pearson correlation coefficient
    c. nonparametric test; Spearman rank-order correlation coefficient
    d. nonparametric test; Mann-Whitney U test

36. The **Mann-Whitney *U* test** is used when there are two groups, a _____ -groups design, and an _____ variable.
    a. within; interval
    b. between; interval
    c. within; ordinal
    d. between; ordinal

37. Which of the following is NOT an assumption for the Mann-Whitney *U* test?
    a. We should use random selection.
    b. Difference scores should come from a symmetric population distribution.
    c. The data must be ordinal.
    d. Ideally, no ranks are tied.

38. In a Mann-Whitney *U* test with 7 participants in each group, a *p* level of 0.05 and a two-tailed test, our critical value is:
    a. 8.
    b. 11.
    c. 10.
    d. 13.

39. In a Mann-Whitney *U* test, if we have 12 people in each group and $U = 40$ with a *p* level of 0.05 and a two-tailed test, we would:
    a. reject the null hypothesis.
    b. be unable to make a decision regarding the outcome of the test.
    c. need to compare ΣR_1 and ΣR_2 first.
    d. fail to reject the null hypothesis.

40. You administer a test of math abilities to two groups of 6 students and will analyze the data using a Mann-Whitney *U* test. Group 1 earns the following scores: 19, 17, 16, 13, 12, 7. Group 2 earns the following scores: 16, 14, 12, 11, 9, 5. Based on this information, ΣR_1 and ΣR_2 would be, respectively:
    a. 31; 47.
    b. 30; 48.
    c. 47; 31.
    d. 48; 30.

41. You measure the amount of time that it takes two groups of rats to run through a maze and analyze the data using a Mann-Whitney *U* test. Group 1 earns the following times: 5.2, 5.7, 6.1, 6.2, 6.8, 7.3, 7.7. Group two earns the following times: 6.5, 6.6, 7.2, 7.8, 8.4, 8.8, 8.9. Based on this information, *U* would equal:
    a. 36.
    b. 69.
    c. 8.
    d. 41.

42. Which of the following is the formula for calculating U in a Mann-Whitney U test for the first group?

   a. $U_1 = (n_1)(n_1) + \dfrac{n_1(n_1 + 1)}{2} - \sum R_1$

   b. $U_1 = (n_1)(n_2) + \dfrac{n_1(n_1 + 1)}{2} - \sum R_1$

   c. $U_1 = (n^2) + \dfrac{n_1(n_1 + 1)}{2} - \sum R_1$

   d. $U_1 = \dfrac{n_1(n_1 + 1)}{2} - \sum R_1$

ANSWERS TO CHAPTER 15 STUDY QUESTIONS

Question Number	Correct Answer	Question Number	Correct Answer
1	a, pp. 403–404	22	a, pp. 411–414
2	a, pp. 403–404	23	c, p. 412
3	c, p. 404	24	c, p. 413
4	d, p. 404	25	b, p. 413
5	b, p. 404	26	d, p. 413
6	b, p. 405	27	d, p. 415
7	d, p. 405	28	c, p. 415
8	c, p. 406	29	c, p. 418
9	b, p. 406	30	c, p. 418
10	a, p. 406	31	b, p. 419
11	c, p. 407	32	d, p. 419
12	a, pp. 407–410	33	d, pp. 419–420
13	c, pp. 407–410	34	b, p. 420
14	c, p. 408	35	d, p. 421
15	a, p. 408	36	d, p. 421
16	b, p. 409	37	b, p. 421
17	c, p. 409	38	a, pp. 422–423
18	a, pp. 410, 415	39	d, pp. 422–424
19	a, p. 411	40	a, pp. 423–424
20	d, p. 411	41	c, pp. 423–424
21	a, p. 411	42	b, p. 424